Carrie Ekins

Hot Mess Alchemist

The Mind Body Reasons Why You Are Feeling Overwhelmed And Under Stress

For Bear, first & always.

I'm lucky enough to have been firmly supported, cheerleaded and loved on (even when I'm running around, getting in my own way!) by a tribe of truly tremendous women.
Massive gratitude to Lady Playpiece, my Faith Keepers & to Kate Arbuckle - every Alchemist needs a Kate.

Contents

1.	Alchemist, you're a Hot Mess	4
2.	Slink like a Tiger	12
3.	The Socially Engineered Woman	21
4.	The Leg Bone's Connected To The Ankle Bone	33
5.	Don't Panic!	41
6.	Boo Hiss Patriarchy!	58
7.	External Environment vs Internal Landscape	65
8.	Becoming Aligned	72
9.	Watch Out! Someone's Trying To 'Should' On You!	79
10.	Choices, Choices	89
11.	There's A Lot Of Bricks In Rome	103
12.	Work Your Magic	108
13.	The Secret Of Tomato Saucery	119
14.	Bringing It All Together	134

Chapter 1
Alchemist, you're a hot mess!

If you're the kind of person that leaves an inadvertent trail of burnt toast in your wake, then this book may be for you.

If you're the kind of person that feels LIKE burnt toast; dry, overdone and crispy - then this book is DEFINITELY for you.

Welcome, Hot Mess Alchemist, to a world that understands you, and meets your crispy crust lifestyle with empathy and compassion.

Now, some of you may be reading this and wondering if you are a) a Hot Mess, b) an Alchemist or c) A Hot Mess & an Alchemist? Let's explore. I've met a lot of Alchemists in my time - not the literal, historical figures who are on a mission to create gold from base metals, but those shiny souls that create metaphorical gold in their lives and the lives of those they shine upon.

An Alchemist is a daring, caring, transformational being. They've constantly got a million ideas and creative projects floating around and whizzing about. Their interest lies in creating, making and enjoying this wild trip called life much more than they're interested in curating it, structuring it and making it fit into tidy boxes.

The thing is, sometimes all this joyous living of life can feel a bit overwhelming. It's not in your nature to go around imposing structure on things, as it's so much more enjoyable to stay loose and free. And yeah, sometimes this can feel messy, which is totally fine until you have to deal with the rest of the world!

Because unfortunately most Alchemists live in a world that requires interaction with others, and that takes organisation to some degree - especially if you have family commitments. You need some kind of, for want of a better word, strategy to help you navigate the day to day which has the bonus of keeping you feeling grounded and in control, otherwise the mildly contained chaos can over flow into overstimulation, over thinking and over spill - a total Hot Mess situation! But you still require it to allow you to be as magical as fuck - because that's your special sauce.

Maybe you've been accused of being a little 'head in the clouds' or a 'daydreamer', and that's left you with a sense that maybe you can't be taken seriously? What I'm here to remind you of is this: you have the power to create amazing things, you don't have to play by the rules written by, historically, a white, straight, male system.

The thing about the label 'Alchemist', and let's be clear, it's an arbitrary label - you can take it or leave it, but it is kind of a fun one! Anyhoo, the thing about it is that even though you know who you are, you might also wonder if you are truly weird enough.

It's an irony isn't it, to feel like the peculiar one at the work event, or family social or at the school gates, with that uneasy feeling that people just wouldn't 'get you' if you said what was really occupying your thoughts. But at the same time you don't feel 'wacky', 'zany', eccentric enough to truly be counted as Weird, especially not 'cool weird', which by equal measure you envy and despise.

The crux of the matter is you have so much to share and so much good to do but you just can't get it out in the world without feeling scatty, pointless and not very good at being a 'proper' grown up whilst at the same time unable to fully embody your kooky, quirky side?

If that sounds familiar then you've come to the right place for a reframe.

Why?

Because, I believe:

- You can be playful and an expert in your field.
- You can feel right at home in your body - confident, clear and grounded, whilst having a full rosta of life going on.
- And you can do the work and live the life you want to live. One that feels spacious and joyous and not a total suck of your energy.
- You know that 'normal' is boring and you want to live a life that feels like a carnival of delights, and that is totally within your power.

You want to know why I believe this? Because time and time again I have seen that the only thing that stands between you and your dream, is you.

Everything you need is inside of you, which may come as a shock because you've probably spent years, decades even, thinking that all the answers lie outside, away from you. Y'know, everything will be great when…: you've got that promotion; or when people recognise your talent; when he/she/they realise they love you. It's always on the horizon, it's always over the freaking rainbow. You feel like you're chasing, chasing, chasing. But the answers aren't outside of you, they're not waiting for the correct planetary alignment. The answers are here. In you. It really is an inside job.

I also believe that a lot of the puzzle pieces you may be requiring are here, with me. My super power is helping you to unlock your magic.

For many folk whether you're living in a suburban world that smells vaguely of tumble dryer sheets or out in the sticks, it can feel immensely vulnerable to feel removed enough from the norm to be 'quirky' and yet at the same time, not feel able to own your weirdness enough to stand with the Weird. As a response you get quiet, you go inward, you shut down how freaking magical you are.

You, Me, We deny our gifts.

Well, my love, personally I got sick of playing shy and small. I wanted to be the freaking Unicorn I KNOW I am. I'm not talking magical horned ponies cantering around bloody Avalon. I'm talking about creative, gorgeous, shiny, wise, gifted beings that have a wealth of love and talent to share.

Beings like you whose power lies in seeing the world from a unique angle, with curiosity and wonder at the very heart of it.

Just. Like. You.

No matter how secure and loving your childhood might have been, oftentimes you, we, all of us grow up feeling that there are bits of ourselves we don't 'get'. Whilst that's natural it can also lead us to second guessing ourselves and you find yourself in a world of doubt. If you find yourself saying "If only...", "I should...", "I wish...", well keep reading and you'll find ways to flip those same words over to make them "I can...", "I am..." and "Oh, just watch me shine....".

I know how you struggle to take all the magic making energy you have inside of you and turn it into something that pays the bills and yet still feels true to who you really are. I know it, because I've been there myself. This book is about sorting through all that gunk that is smothering your wild abilities, all the crap that's holding you at arm's length from the life you really want, and bringing you closer to who you really wish to be.

Hot Mess Alchemist is a book of playful strategy and curious introspection. Through its pages we'll look at the reasons you're holding yourself back and apply uncomplicated methods so you can:

- prioritise your own needs
- let go of the stories that you're 'too scatty' to get what you want
- trust your brilliance
- discover the best soul medicine you can get for free
- do the 'thing' even when you're bricking it
- become organised without the overwhelm
- keep going til you get where you want to be.

I'm rooting for you to become a less messy Alchemist. You deserve to experience your magic and the world requires it too.

You may think you're the most vanilla thing since Vanilla Ice Cream, but think about what vanilla really is: A potent, unmistakable flavour, from a rare orchid, which in its true form is wildly expensive because it's so prized, and whilst you can buy the synthetic form for cheap as chips it's nowhere near as good as the real thing. You're not synthetic, you are the real, rare, deal.

You're pure vanilla - an exotic elevation. Own that shit. Your hot messiness is just your magic run through everyone else's filters, so change the filter and own your magic.

In this book, we're going to draw back the curtain on the bullshit you've been fed since you were a tiny tot. All those unwritten rules, and the very much spoken rhetoric, that diminishes you and wants to keep you feeling small and playing small. It's my determination to empower you with an understanding of your physiology that will make sense of why you feel overwhelmed and stressed, and what you can do about it.

Plus, there's a free workbook to accompany the exercises - it's full of tips and tools that will create feel good systems and structures that uphold your brilliance and enable you to keep grounded and productive. You can get access to the workbook at https://courses.carrieekins.co.uk/courses/hotmessworkbook

Ready to make some magic?

Chapter 2
Slink like a Tiger

I'm a really touchy feely person - heck you don't spend two decades of your adult life as a massage therapist if you don't like touching people! What I mean though, is that I'm kinesthetic. I like to get into the physical and not just metaphorically, so throughout this book I'm going to be asking you to get involved by moving your glorious body around.

For me one of the characteristics of feeling like a Hot Mess is the sense of overwhelm and indecision it brings. It's about overthinking and not taking action. It shapes up as inconsistency and a lack of self belief. A Hot Mess attitude puts more value on the thoughts, beliefs and values of the surrounding culture, and through constantly seeking external validation, instead of looking introspectively and realising that if you can calm the panic inside of you, you already have access to a shed load of brilliance.

For many years now when I work hands on with a client I set the intention that we're going to create 'Slink in their system'.

Slink?

What is this Slink?

Do you get what I mean?
Do you FEEL what I mean?

Because Slink is such a word of feeling. It's
practically onomatopoeic (try spelling that in a hurry
- certainly not a slinky word, more of a chewy one).
Y'see. THAT is exactly what I mean.

You can feel the word Slink can't you?
Wanna play along?

If you put your feet on the floor and close your eyes
for a sec, then merely THINK of the word Slink, you
get a sense of it THROUGH your BODY.

In fact, this is a game I ask my clients to play
sometimes. Imagine if you will, that you have a tail
like a tiger, with a certain heaviness when you
swish it. Now take a walk around the room with
your tiger tail, feel how it would pull your tailbone
down, balancing out the tilt of your pelvis.
Allow your pelvis to move like that; give it some hip
sway and looseness.

If you need a visual cue, think about slinking and
prowling through the wilds of your suburban ~~kitchen~~
jungle.

There! You've got it! That's some Tiger energy in your step.

Oh yeah, don't hold back. Suddenly you're a tiger, in the undergrowth. Stalking your prey. Quiet. Focused. Aligned with all of nature.

Imagine Slinking your way through life. It's not arrogant. There's no peacock crying and bustling of feathers. It's assured. It's whole. It's a sense of living life fully. With your finger on the pulse of "Oh yeah" and "Right now".

The same quiet focus and alignment with your desire, as a tiger has stalking a particularly juicy meal. It's the same confidence and readiness to move swiftly.

And what happens when the Tiger misses its prey and crashes short of its target? Not much. It just prowls majestically off, finds a good spot to nap, and THAT'S slinky too.

Slink is not just about limber hips and loose muscles; it's also a state of mind - they're completely intertwined with the other. That's why in my sessions I offer both mentoring for your thoughts and work for your body.

Because confidence in your body, in its slink, its strength and its ability to support you physically, brings out greater confidence in your ability to support yourself mentally and emotionally, and in your ability to go out and create change in your life. You become aware of new possibilities (to succeed) when you feel confident about the things you'd like to change, and achieve.

That feeling is fundamental to our work here. It's about strategy as much as it's about handing you the tools to get you from Hot Mess to Slinky Wee Beastie.

The Mind Body Connection is a term often touted, but often it's poo pooed for its woo woo.

Come play with me, I'd love you to experience the wonder that is the connection between how you feel in your thoughts and how you feel in your physical body. It's a jaw dropper, I'm telling ya, but it could also be a game changer.

If you'd rather be guided through this, there's an audio version in the workbook.[1]

So, if you're able, stand up in a space where you have enough room to hold your arm out straight in front of you and be able to swing around in an arc without whacking anyone in the face. Bring your

---

[1] If you haven't already downloaded the free workbook, you can find it at
https://courses.carrieekins.co.uk/courses/hotmessworkbook

feet shoulder width apart so you feel stable and grounded.

The first thing we're going to do is get a baseline measure of how far you can rotate your body whilst you have your arm up in the air. Bring your arm up in front of you, let's call this 12 o'clock, and at shoulder height. Now, without moving your legs or your hips (as much as possible) you're going to rotate your upper body around to the left, as though your arm is moving through 11 o'clock, 10 o'clock and so forth.

The aim is to keep the arm locked at the shoulder so the movement is coming from the ribs, rather than allowing the arm to flail at the shoulder joint. It helps if you keep looking at your fingertips as you turn. You want to rotate as far as comfortable, so don't over stretch or over rotate. Take a moment to get a sense of how far you've turned.

Alrighty, bring yourself back to forward facing and let's do it in the opposite direction. Swap arms, bringing it up to shoulder height in front of you and moving from the upper body start to rotate to the right. Or to the left if you've already rotated right - there's always a couple of us that move the other way first, it's all good!

Again sweep the body and arm around as though you're a hand on a clock pointing to the hours. Remember to keep your hips and feet forward facing. Only rotate as far as feels comfortable and once you're there, take a moment to appreciate how far you've turned. Then bring it back to the centre.

Hokay, so you've just found your baseline, how your body feels when you're focused on an instruction but in a neutral state of mind. Now, we're going to bring emotion into the game and see whether there's any change.

For our next round of rotations I'd like you to take a minute or so and conjure up a memory. Close your eyes, and allow yourself to think about a time when you felt super positive; you may have felt: happy; contented; pleased; loved or celebrated. Whatever it was, really allow yourself to be flooded with positivity.

Got it?

Great!

Let's retest.

Remember, feet shoulder width apart. Arm raised up in front of you to shoulder height. Hips are going to stay firmly fixed as you rotate your upper body. Don't let your shoulder flap your arm about, keep it connected to the body as you turn, like the hand of a clock. Once again, rotate as far as you feel comfortable, keep looking at your fingertips, and when you feel like you've reached the end of your rotation don't forget to take a moment and mentally mark how far you've turned.

Good stuff!

So return to your start point and let's do it in the opposite direction. All the way to the end of the range of motion whilst you keep your thoughts in that happy, positive place. Aaaand again, take a moment to see how far you rotated.

Alrighty, return to the starting point, drop your arm and take a breath. So, did this round of arm rotating feel any different to the first round? Could you move as far, could you move further? Did it feel the same or was there a different quality to the movement?

Ready for the third round?

This time, if you feel willing, I'd like you to conjure up a negative experience. If you're comfortable to do so, take yourself back to a memory that evokes feelings of sadness or sorrow. Once you're there, we're going to retest.

Same as before, arm raised in front of you to shoulder height, feet planted shoulder width apart. Hold on to the emotion as you rotate your upper body to the end of what feels comfortable. Then bring yourself back to the starting point and rotate in the opposite direction. Keep the arm moving with the upper body, don't allow it to flap around, with your eyes looking at your fingertips.

So, what did you find?

Did you feel as though your arm rotated as far as the two previous tests or less far? Did it feel smooth and easy or heavy? Have a think and take a moment to verbalise it in your own words.

I've been using this game with clients for years, it's such a great way of demonstrating how connected our thoughts and movement are. What we experience on an emotional or mental level can have a significant impact on how we feel and function on a physical level. Clients often mention that the positive round feels smooth and easy and they're surprised by how much further their body is able to turn and yet the negative round often feels clunky, heavy and they don't seem to turn as far.

Isn't that interesting?!? You've just dictated to your body how it should feel by simply conjuring up an emotion - not even by experiencing an actual situation that would authentically bring up those feelings.

Now, there is much argument as to whether you can 'fake it til you make it' in life, and I'm not sure. But what I am confident of is that you have more power over your life than you might give yourself credit for.

Being aware of how your emotions are affecting how you feel in your body, or putting some slink in your step may not give you the confidence levels of socialite scammer Anna Delvey, but they've certainly got the ability to create ease and confidence in yourself and that's an amazing start. I think that we have overlooked the mind-body connection for a really long time because it can be inconvenient to think about our feelings and emotions and it's much easier to move swiftly along and rationalise the shit out of a thing. We've been told that that's the road to progression, it needs to be quick and controlled, but our very nature requires space and time to process, which is what we're going to look at in greater detail in the next chapters.

Chapter 3
The Socially Engineered Woman.

GAAAAHHHHH! STRESSS!!!

Holy shoot! Now there's a pandemic going on right there. Stress, Mental Health, Emotional Wellbeing, Trauma. There is a LOT of it going on.

Generations of us have been told as children to 'Suck it up', that only 'babies' cry, we expect better from big girls like you, Boys don't cry. There's so much rhetoric here. Just think about aaaaalll the stories you were told as a kid.

And I get it, these are words uttered to help us 'build character'. As parents we do it, just as our parents did it, and our grandparents too, it goes back through time. Even strangers in the street feel compelled to tell wailing tots to cheer up because no one likes to see tears.

But Bleurrrrghhhh! It makes me so fricking mad. Our emotions are seen as inconvenient from a very early age. We pride ourselves, in the UK, on having a stiff upper lip and that we can Keep Calm & Carry

On! (That's actual war propaganda my friend, straight from a 1939 motivational poster from the British wartime Ministry of Information[2]).

Women have been labelled as hysterical (Thanks Freud, and even he was calling in the Greek Philosophers there.) or 'overly emotional'. It's seen as a direct response to our hormonal makeup, something to be endured and trained out of.

In fact, if you're wondering how long this emotional bullshit has been perpetuated, we can easily take it all the way back to the Ancient Greeks.

Let's start with Aristotle.

Aristotle was a misogynist. Fact. He was incredibly interested in human biology, which he studied by studying animals. For Aristotle women were 'deformed men'[3], wearing their testicles on the inside (ovaries). He believed women to be second class, due to their lesser strength and their 'cold' wetness - menstrual blood. The Greeks were, frankly, a bit obsessed with female blood and their monthly bleed. Primarily because the successful

---

[2] The story behind 'Keep Calm and Carry On' | University of London *(accessed on 4/7/23)*

[3] Colette A, Women & Misogyny in Ancient Greek Philosophy. November 2017. Available at https://womeninantiquity.wordpress.com/2018/11/27/women-and-misogyny-in-ancient-greek-philosophy/ *(accessed on 4/7/23)*

production of progeny was seen as the only really useful role for a woman.

The earliest 'medics', the Hippocratics, believed that blood soaked into a woman via her skin and then was released once a month, unless she was pregnant in which case the blood would nourish the baby[4]. The Hippocratics wrote, in the 'Epidemics' that women accumulated a large amount of blood in their breasts, which made them irrational. Men on the other hand did not, which accounted for them being far more rational.

It was believed that without enough intercourse, a woman's womb would become light and dry, and could travel around the body, the worst symptom of which would be hysteria. Now, you might be reading this and having a giggle - those Greeks were nuts right?

The problem is, this shit stuck. The laws of Ancient Greece institutionalised inequality and it feels like it's still prevalent. Women were second class citizens, valued only just above slaves. Rape culture was rife[5], the punishment for which was

---

[4] Stecewicz L. Women's Health and Religious Healing. November 2020. Available at: https://womeninantiquity.wordpress.com/2020/11/15/womens-health-and-religious-healing/ *(accessed on 4/7/23)*

[5] MCM312, Consent and Rape Culture in Ancient Greece. December 2017Available at: https://womeninantiquity.wordpress.com/2017/12/06/consent-and-rape-culture-in-ancient-greece/ *(accessed on 4/7/23)*

often a fine which would be paid to the Guardian of the assaulted woman (either her father or her husband). A Greek woman had no representation in a court, nor in the Symposium (a social gathering where men would drink, eat and be entertained). The only accounts of Greek Women available are those drawn through the male observer. Everything was filtered by men.

Whilst some philosophers, such as Socrates and Plato were progressive, others like Aristotle held deep seated misogynistic views. It was Aristotle's belief that only men were capable of rational thought, and only men were fit to lead and rule. Women were subordinate to men, only slightly more useful than slaves or children.

Aristotle also touches on the status of women in *History of Animals IX*. He asserts his beliefs in the character flaws inherent to women and states that men are more virtuous, braver, and intelligent than their female counterparts. He attributes compassion and emotionality to women, along with a lack of critical ability, and believed women to be impressionable, easily deceived, and feeble of mind.

Ancient Greek thought was still highly prized in modern western Academia well into the early 1900s, which is both lazy and awful. Between this and a treatise written in 1486 by Heinrich Kramer called the Malleus Maleficarum, women have been hounded and typecast for millenia.

The Malleus Maleficarum, or Hammer of the Witches, was a compendium of demonology and witchcraft written by a Catholic clergyman. It stated that witchcraft and magic were delusions and those who believed in such things had been "seduced by the Devil in dreams and visions"[6].

Now, many treaties against witchcraft had been written before then, but what makes the Malleus Maleficarum so different is that it was the original pulp fiction. The advent of the printing press meant that thousands of copies could be printed, and distributed at a reasonable price[7]. This in turn put it into the hands of many misogynistic nutjobs spread far across Europe.

As it goes, Kramer had previously attempted to prosecute alleged witches in Austria and had, in fact, been run out of the Tyrol by his Bishop who dismissed him as senile and crazy[8]. He wrote Malleus as an act of revenge and self justification and it worked. It gave him expert status. The Pope

---

[6] Wikipedia. Available at:
https://en.wikipedia.org/wiki/Malleus_Maleficarum *(accessed on 4/7/23)*
[7] Gatehouse G, The Coming Storm, BBC production. December 2021. Available at
https://www.bbc.co.uk/sounds/series/m001324r
[8] The 'Hammer of Witches': An Earthquake in the Early Witch Craze – The Historian (qmul.ac.uk) *(accessed on 4/7/23)*

was so impressed that he gave Kramer full papal permission to run Inquisitions and drive out witchcraft. Prior to the 1400s it was rare for Witches to be trialled. Post Malleus Maleficarum, it practically became a sport.

Hokay, So the point of the chapter isn't about ridiculous males making up arbitrary rules of what makes women 'worthy' - but if you were wondering why you feel subjected to judgement and scorn, well it's truly historic. As magical nurturing women, we've been cast as witches, and weaklings, and because our views and intellect are so scary to the male ego and societal power structures, they've literally written us out of history, or reported us via the male interpretation of our words. We've been made into the devil's sidekick and the demon herself.

Right! Speaking of outdated folklore, let's challenge the standard interpretation of the Human Nervous System, which is often described as being in Fight and Flight OR Rest and Digest. Newer research points to a polyvagal system that incorporates both the sympathetic and parasympathetic sides of the nervous system working concurrently. THIS IS HUGE.

Ahh you see, now I'm getting all giddy and ahead of myself! Let's take a breath and come back to our bodies.

Now, this is a pure tool for life, and one that can help you through a hard day for sure.

Place both feet on the ground, with or without socks - as you choose. Get comfy, either stood up, sat down or laid down with your knees bent.

First step is to feel into your feet. Wiggle your toes, and as you do, become aware of the surface beneath them. How does it feel? Rough? Smooth? Granular? Can you feel the shine of a well worn carpet pile? Or the cool touch of tile?

Now become aware of the inside of your feet. As you squish them around on the floor are there achy parts, painful parts, joints that click? Does it feel as though your toes are resting into the ground as equally as your heels? Does it feel as though more of your body weight is connecting through the left foot, the right foot or equally between the two?

Bring your attention now to the top of your head. Tuck in your chin and visualise the crown of your head being drawn away from your tailbone.

Now take a hand and place it on your chest with your fingers lightly resting just below your collar bones. After a moment or so see if you can register the heat of your fingers, the hardness of the heel of your palm. Let your hand melt into your chest, visualise them melding together. If you can toggle your brain between the heat of your body and the temperature of your hand, see if you can sense them balancing each other out.

Okay, that should only take a minute or two once you've practised. All you're required to do now is breathe. Not even fancy, complicated 'count whilst you do it' breathing. Just let the air slide into your lungs and out again. Then the magic happens all of its own accord! You'll notice after a few ins and outs that your breathing seems to deepen, the breath naturally drops further into your body. You might experience your tummy start to rise and fall. The jittery energy of the day will level out, it's awesome!

Here's a secret (ssshhhhhh!), this is just between us Alchemists. I demonstrate this technique a LOT when I give talks and teach, not only because it's a blooming mega tool for life, but also because I need it. You may have noticed, I get a bit giddy, and when I do, my words come out in a jumble, I dip from one topic to another. This one technique gets me back to a calm, focused headspace everytime. My voice drops a couple of tones, I feel gathered and grounded, I'm able to convey my thoughts with clarity. This technique really is every public speaker's best friend!

So, I mentioned early on that I'm a massage therapist specialising in Myofascial Release - which may not be a concept you've heard of before. The Myofascia is the covering of every muscle in the body, it connects everything. Think of it as a wrapper: every cell has a fascial wrapping know as the cell membrane; the heart has the pericardium, the gut is contained within a kind of bag made of fascia; every organ, muscle, ligament, tendon and squishy bit has a fascial wrapper.

Did you know that you can follow a single sheet of this fascial wrapping from the sole of the foot all the way up to the eyebrow?[9] Seriously. It starts as the plantar fascia, moves up to cover the gastrocnemius muscle of the calf, then the hamstrings, it covers the gluteus (bum) muscles, works its way over and up the erector spinae muscles either side of the spine, until it reaches the neck where it finally becomes the covering of the scalp. True story.

As a Myofascial Release therapist, I'm interested in where there are snags on these big sheets of fascia. Because where there's scar tissue or gunked up tissue you'll find a puckering and a lack of softness, which in turn will drag the softer surrounding tissue in towards it. The onward effect of this is wonkiness, pain and discomfort.

Now wait for it, I'm about to blow your mind! The fascia of the body is like a massive communication system and interacts with other body systems such

---

[9] Myers, T. Anatomy Trains: Myofascial Meridians for Manual Therapists and Movement Professionals. 2001.

as the nervous system. However, we're only starting to learn more about this incredible system as medical research techniques have evolved in the past few decades. Amazing huh!?

It's not that the fascia is a new discovery, it's always been there, but it's been overlooked as just the annoying white stuff medical researchers would scrape away during dissection. To be honest our understanding of it has grown since we've started to look at the entire body as connected and in relationship. Apart from this there's another couple of good reasons for our greater understanding (plot spoiler - the Patriarchy is involved!).

I'm going to paraphrase slightly, because it's all kind of long winded, and really if we set me off I could end up writing a very different book! Primarily though, the Catholic church got a bit freaked out with all these keen scientists getting curious about the body. The body belonged to Christ right?! Who were these dudes with scalpels intent on cutting dead folk up, and all in the name of 'science'! So it was decreed that whilst the mind, body and spirit belonged to God, these young upstarts could chop up bits of the body - but not work on an intact human. So research happened a part at a time - which meant that everything was seen in isolation.

The second part of the puzzle was solved when the technology of medical research became smart enough to allow scientists to look inside a live body.

Remember, most of what we know about the human anatomy and physiology has been derived from cadaver studies i.e dead people.

There's something you may not have thought about before and it's this, in comparison to a living human, a dead body is very dry. Fascia in its alive state is incredibly moist, it's really hydrophilic i.e. it loves water and needs it to operate at optimal levels of squish. Dry, deceased fascia shrivels up, it looks different, it feels different and it's almost impossible to make sense of its importance. If you're curious about what living, working fascia looks like, I can highly recommend you watch "Strolling under the Skin" by Dr Jean-Claude Guimberteau on YouTube[10].

Further research by the likes of Peter Levine[11] and Besel Van Der Kolke[12] has pointed to the effect of trauma upon the physical body - and by trauma, I don't just mean physical wrenching, but also emotional, mental and spiritual trauma. This is stored at a cellular level in the tissue of the body. In the FASCIA of the body.

---

[10] Guimberteau JC. Strolling Under The Skin. December 2019. Available at: https://youtu.be/DroKc3w0-dA *(accessed on 4/7/23)*

[11] Try 'Waking The Tiger: Healing Trauma' by Peter Levine, 1997

[12] 'The Body Keeps The Score' by Bessel Van Der Kolke, 2014 changed everything for me.

The body is literally the page on which your life has been written.

Imagine that, within you, stored in deep pockets are old memories of trauma, beliefs, experiences (both positive and negative). In my treatment room I call it Spelunking - an Americanism for Potholing (which to my mind is a weird, very British, very scary sounding term and quite honestly does not hold half the romance of the idea of Spelunking, which I borrowed from an American client).

Spelunking is about reaching into the old, tight gunk of the body, releasing the tightness, allowing the fabric of the body to heal itself. It's not uncommon for my clients to recollect old memories which may relate to previous injury, there's often metaphor and recognition of old patterns of thought that no longer serve them. Together we do the work that allows them to let go of old hurts, in all forms, and create something that is a lighter, brighter, more positive way of experiencing the world.

Over the next couple of chapters we're going to start to explore the human nervous system and how the physiology of it all ties together with our beliefs and social conditioning. It's going to be a fast ride, hold on to your hats!

Chapter 4
The Leg Bone's Connected To The Ankle Bone.
The Mind Bone's Connected To The Body Bone.
The Nervous System Is Connected To
Everything.

Ahhh of all the chapters in this book, this is the one that in my determination to get right has stressed me out most. Which is an irony, because we're going to take a look at your nervous system.

Here's the thing. Thinking about what stresses us out can be stressful, partially because we think we 'should' be able to get a better handle on things (hey there other people's limiting beliefs presented to our malleable minds during childhood!) but there's also a physiological thing going on.

Think about the body's nervous system: you may know about the concept of 'fight or flight' and you might have heard of 'rest and digest' too. At school we get fed the story that our stress response is either 'On' or 'Off', depending on whether we're running away from a bear or chilling in our cave.

It's pretty binary as far as high school biology explanations go.

Problem is, it doesn't explain what you're actually feeling, does it? It's confusing to be having a nice time hanging out with your buddies and yet still feel anxious, isn't it? That's because it isn't an 'on/off' flip the switch situation, it's more complicated than that.

Don't panic about it though, I'm going to walk you through enough knowledge for you to understand what's broadly going on, without it feeling like a lecture (hopefully!). And there's a 'map' of your nervous system in the Hot Mess Workbook - you can find it here at https://courses.carrieekins.co.uk/courses/hotmessw orkbook

Alrighty! Let's begin.

Your nervous system has developed over hundreds of millions of years. It's the body's command centre sending messages and demands out across the entire body via the brain, spinal cord and the nerves. Your spinal cord is a bundle of nerves protected from harm by the bony spinal column. The cord acts like a major highway with task related nerves branching off at each vertebrae.

We talk about the brain and the spinal cord as a subsystem of the Central Nervous System, and then the radiating nerves which send and receive information from every part of the body are known as the Peripheral Nervous System (PNS).

Within the PNS we have the Somatic Nervous System (SNS) which guides the movements of muscles, and the Autonomic Nervous System (ANS), which is responsible for automatic activities that take place without thought. Plus a third branch called the Enteric Nervous System (ENS), whose function is concerned with digesting food and absorbing nutrients.

The building blocks of the Nervous System are called Neurons. They're specialised cells that send electrical signals that travel between your brain, the spinal cord, skin, organs, glands and muscles, relaying information back and forth.

There are different neurons for different tasks. Motor neurons look after movement. Sensory neurons take information from your senses, via the eyes, ears, nose, mouth and skin and send that information up to the brain. Other specialist neurons take command of automatic tasks, such as breathing, digestion, shivering when cold, and regulating your heartbeat.

From an evolutionary perspective, the first part of the human brain to develop, (sometimes nicknamed the Lizard brain, which includes the brain stem), handles the unconscious, automatic activities that you need to exist, for example: breathing and stimulation of the muscles that relate to blood supply. This area is concerned with your survival, it's constantly receiving information from your senses and making decisions about whether the world is a safe place. It's ready to send signals, both neural via the nervous system, and chemicals such as hormones, to any part of the body required to ensure that you live long enough to procreate and continue your blood line.

The standard explanation of the Autonomic Nervous System will tell you that there are three parts to the Autonomic nervous system: the Enteric Nervous System that governs the function of the gastrointestinal tract; the Sympathetic Nervous System (SNS) and the Parasympathetic Nervous System (PNS). In the traditional explanation, the Sympathetic and Parasympathetic systems are in relationship, it's kind of like a 'Push-Me-Pull-You' - they operate together but separately, balancing each other out.

For instance the PNS will speed up the rate at which your heart beats, whilst the SNS will slow down your heart rate, depending on whether you are relaxed or running away from a sabre tooth tiger. The PNS will suppress the activity of your digestive system (handy if you're fighting for your life), whilst the SNS will activate your digestion once you are safe.

So if you find yourself in a stress response the PNS is 'in charge' - it lowers your libido (because you're too busy worrying about your own life to be in a position to create and raise a new life), you don't feel hungry (who has time to process food!) and your breathing becomes shallow.

On the flip side, once danger has passed, the SNS takes control. Digestion kicks in (if you've ever wondered why your tummy starts rumbling and gurgling during a massage, it's a side effect of the relaxation you're experiencing), your breath drops deeper into your lungs - funnily enough, once you know this you can cheat your way out of stress, I'll show you how in a bit. And the idea of sexy time just for the heck of it sounds like an inviting prospect again!

It's all very on and off isn't it. How very tidy! However, in reality it isn't this convenient, but it is still simple.

Here's a thing for you to bear in mind. Like I said, your brain has evolved incrementally over millions and millions of years. And up until the Industrial Revolution, life was pretty much 'what you see is what you get'. The advent of electricity, the motor car, television, and other technological gizmos, has changed everything. Add the evolution of the Digital Age and Holy Mary, Mother of Geoff, your nervous system is pranging out!

Because, and how's this for wild, the deepest, oldest parts of your brain responsible for judging how life threatening a situation is, have not caught up in evolutionary terms. Your brain can not compute how much society has changed in the past 10, 30, 50 years - think about it, 50 years ago it was still rare to have a phone at home, the first text message was sent in 1992 and Facebook didn't exist before 2004. Technology and all the pressures that brings with it is comparatively new, and it's just one facet in the myriad of changes we have experienced in recent times.

Your brain, however, literally doesn't perceive the difference between a deadline at work and a mammoth attack. It could be an email notification, it could be a tiger for all your brain knows. Job interviews, traffic jams, scary movies, fights on EastEnders, white knuckle rollercoasters - your brain doesn't have a facking clue whether it's trivial or the end is nigh. So it takes its best punt and has you running around metaphorically shouting "We're all DOOMED" like Chicken Licken, under an Oak tree, in September.

No wonder you're knackered.

Because it doesn't stop there. Now there is all this stimulus bombarding your system, constantly, twenty four hours a day if you allow it - the creepy thing is, even though your nervous system hates a lot of our modern accoutrements like screens, devices and sneaky, tricksome apps (I'm looking at you Candy Crush, Gala Bingo and Bet Fred), it also really, REALLY likes them, thanks to those clever programmers - DING DING DING DOPAMINE HIGH!!! And so there's no let up, we are both sucked in and freaked out all at once.

Plus humans have become conditioned to KEEP GOING!! Even if the proverbial hits the fan, we have been conditioned to suck it up and continue ONWARDS! I mean, keeping those wheels of industry turning is the main thing, am I right?? No, I'm not right. But that's what we've been taught to think. Consider all the bullshit encouragements we tell ourselves and each other, particularly us Brits:

- Chin up
- Stiff Upper lip (what even is that anyhow??)
- Straighten Up
- Stand Tall
- Shoulders back!
- If at first you don't succeed, try try again
- Over the top!

Bleurgh…

Hello, is that the Patriarchy calling? You want your stiff upper lip back? GOOD you can have it!

Mostly what I'm trying to demonstrate here is that, as far as western society is concerned, gold stars and brownie points go to those who are willing to 'soldier on' in the face of adversity - like cannon fodder... We don't listen to our bodies, we don't listen to our nervous system, we don't listen to what our intuition, our gut, is trying to tell us. Some time ago, someone in the top tier of 'life management' decided that our humanness was our biggest weakness and needed to be overcome. That in order to get ahead of the pack, we had to be willing to sacrifice ourselves. That Industry is bigger than the Individual.

The truth is, that kind of thinking is making us sick.

Chapter 5
Don't Panic!!

Lord only knows the world is complicated enough, but we're going to sashay over here, away from the on/off analogy and instead let's feel our way into an explanation that's going to make far more sense to you. All thanks to a guy called Stephen Porges.

Porges, a research psychologist, in the mid 1990s developed a different way of viewing stress, called the Polyvagal model. Let's break that down - Poly meaning many, referring to the many branches of the vagus nerve. Vagus/vagal is Latin meaning 'to wonder', which is appropriate considering how far through the body the nerve travels and the breadth of its influence.

The vagus nerve runs from the brain, through the face, throat, heart and all the way to the viscera of the abdomen. Viscera is another fancy word for the fascia or connective tissue - as we've just discussed the goopy white stuff that up until recently scientists thought was just an inconvenience that required scraping away so they could get to 'the important' stuff when doing dissections.

Traditionally, Science has underestimated how central a role the vagus nerve plays in the nervous system - which was a big mistake, but now it's catching up. Learning about the polyvagal system has the power to change how you respond to the world, and it explains why you tend to beat yourself up for the way you respond. By applying your knowledge of the polyvagal system to your life, so many weird behaviours will now make sense, it's super fun and it can feel like a massive relief.

Alrighty, so previously, the old model was on/off, stressed/not stressed. Or in other words, the two branches of the nervous system: Sympathetic and Parasympathetic, were only compared whilst in different states - one under threat and one in safety. No one spent any time looking at whether the Sympathetic nervous system was playing a pattern in regulating things when there was no stress to respond to, or if the Parasympathetic system had a role when things were stressful. So, according to the old way of looking at the nervous system, the Sympathetic branch 'only' looks after us when 'bad/dangerous' things are happening and the Parasympathetic branch 'only' when 'good/pleasing' things are going on. What if this was a bit simplistic, researchers such as Porges started to wonder.

The polyvagal model takes away that binary dynamic, neither branch is 'Bad', both are imperative for successful, creative life to flourish. Porges is suggesting instead that we need the drive that the sympathetic nervous system gives us: it gets us going; helps us maintain momentum; keeps us on track to complete tasks. Then the parasympathetic nervous system kicks in allowing us to slow down, rest and renew.. But there's more…

Porges has a different take on what is happening as the body responds to stress. As he terms it, there are multiple states of nervous system activation. He suggests that there are three neural circuits that support different types of behaviour. There is Sympathetic Activation (what is commonly thought to be the Sympathetic Nervous System) and then two branches to the Parasympathetic: the Ventral Vagal Social Engagement circuit and the Dorsal Vagal Shutdown circuit, giving a further response to risk or danger.

Here's the absolute kicker, the size of the threat is not the same as the size of the reaction to the threat.

Imagine four people invited to a vaccination session at a local clinic. One person will walk in calm and breezy, have the injection no problem and walk out absolutely fine. The second may feel a little worried on the way there, feel a bit sweaty, heart racing and trembling but within moments of the injection will have shaken that off and will be back to feeling totally normal. The third person may be so terrified of the mere thought of the injection that they dread the appointment for weeks beforehand, walk in white as a sheet, almost refusing to proceed, unable to look at the needle, then feel teary and shaken for an hour or so post injection. The fourth person might take one look at the invitation and point blank refuse due to their fear of doctors, needles and medical procedures being too strong to contemplate. Same level of threat, four completely different levels of response.

We have all met people whose life was negatively impacted by the death of a loved one, and others that have moved on from a death or natural disaster swiftly and with seemingly no negative affect. From the outside, you can never tell how a person will respond to a stressful situation and from the inside a threat may register completely differently from one person to the next. No matter how logical or rational a person is, their nervous system will respond based on previous experience, learnt behaviours from childhood and what they've seen modelled by others. For example, if two people were walking down a street together and happened to be held up at knifepoint - one might fight their assailant and the other might freeze. Same threat, different response.

Okay, Porges illuminates one more branch to the parasympathetic nervous system - the Ventral Vagus Social Engagement circuit, or Social nervous system. Our Social nervous system is guided to look at the people around us, assess their facial expressions and behaviour, and using that, it can then feed back to the brain on whether people are calm and happy, or freaking out. It's a constant cascade, updated in real time; unknowingly you are continuously checking your environment for clues and cues as to whether the world is 'safe' or 'dangerous'.

As Kimberly Anne Johnson points out in her brilliant book 'Call of the Wild'[13] this is one of the many reasons why the Covid Pandemic was so confusing. Wearing face masks meant less facial expression from which to extract information, plus the conflicting states that arise from instinctively wanting to gather closer to others for safety and comfort, whilst at the same time being ordered to maintain physical distance. An absolute 'push me-pull you' of a situation which had to be constantly managed.

Whilst the Sympathetic branch of the nervous system started to develop in creatures 400 million years ago, the social nervous system is the 'newest' branch of the autonomic nervous system -

---

[13] 'Call of the Wild: How we heal trauma, Awaken our own Power and Use it for good' by Kimberly Anne Johnson, Harper Wave, 2021.

having evolved 'only' around 200 million years ago. It's very specific to mammals (those creatures that are warm blooded, give birth to live young and lactate). At an evolutionary level its purpose is to keep a mother loyal to her offspring, therefore improving its chances of survival. It's designed to increase the maternal bond and cooperation by way of facial expressions, so mother and child learn to 'read' each other, and ultimately the child learns to 'read' and interact with the world.

The focus is 'Social' - the clue is in the name. Through the social engagement system our senses are geared to 'read' the environment around us, we learn to use facial expressions as a second, very social, non verbal form of communication, we learn empathy, how to play and how to 'belong'. It wires our brains so we can perceive if the world is safe or dangerous.

If you've ever wondered why your friend goes back to the same awful partner, or why people get stuck in a loop of toxic behaviour - y'know, behaviour that seems illogical, dangerous or downright stupid - the social engagement system is at play. It's an instinctual knowing that you have higher chances of surviving a threat when it is predictable, so it's 'safer' to keep the threat close where you can keep a careful eye on it.

Alrighty, so let's recap:

- Us clever humans have a nervous system that is split into two halves: there's the Central Nervous System (this includes all the automatic processes such as breathing and blood flow) and the Peripheral Nervous System (where we find the Autonomic Nervous System and its component branches and the Somatic Nervous System).
- Within the Autonomic Nervous System there are three branches according to the old model: the Enteric; the Sympathetic and the Parasympathetic
- Aaaaand when we add in our new modern polyvagal model identified by Stephen Porges, we see that the Parasympathetic nervous system has two branches: the Ventral Vagal Social Engagement System (shortened to Social) and the Dorsal Vagal Shutdown circuit, plus the Sympathetic Nervous System which is also known as Sympathetic Activation.

Remember, when your system feels safe, when we're no longer living under threat, perceived or imagined (including holding onto the memory of threat), that's when our bodies can be at their optimal best. If we're stressed, living under perceived threat, our clever, clever sympathetic nervous system will do its damnedest to do what needs to be done to ensure our survival. As we mentioned earlier, modern living is like one stressful occurrence after another - especially for the nervous system that developed between 200 million and 500 million years ago.

Think about it this way:

- 300 million years ago we were living in primitive society doing our best to survive in the face of constant, imminent threat from mammals, other tribes etc.
- 30,000 years ago our societies were exploring representation and storytelling through art.
- 3000 - 2000 years ago, great civilisations such as those in China, Egypt, Greece, the Celts, the Anglo Saxons and the Roman Empire were honouring Gods and honing agriculture, sanitation and the art of war.
- 300 years ago we were prospering from the Agricultural Revolution and the beginnings of the Industrial Revolution.
- 30 years ago we were dreaming of a future full of flying cars and compact discs at the dawn of the digital age.
- 3 years ago mainstream digital culture became the norm, the boundaries of alternative realities and cryptocurrencies were beginning to be pushed and explored.

There are so many things to activate our nervous systems that many people are feeling the effects of compound stress - there is no time, space or importance given to calming or soothing our nervous systems (this process is sometimes referred to as down regulating). It's almost as though relaxation is seen as a luxury or a hobby, rather than a requirement for sustaining our health.

The knock on effect of this is that instead of following our wild instincts and taking time to complete the cycle of the stress response, instead we are indoctrinated to get straight back to full functioning without a pause. There should be three phases to the stress response cycle: First there is the stimuli - 'Look! Sabre Tooth Tiger running this way'; Second 'Gahhhh, I am responding in a way that feels appropriate! Run! Hide! Freeze! Fight! Etc!' and then finally; the third phase should be "Okay guys, let's take a moment to regroup, calm down and check we still have all our limbs. Maybe we should think about how this situation could be avoided in the future? And perhaps we could chill a while, perhaps have a little cry and sacrifice something in gratitude for not being eaten?"

I'm kind of joking, but the third phase is super important. It's a period of physiological regulation during which we decrease the amount of adrenaline, cortisol and other stress hormones floating around in the body, whilst reactivating our digestion and other bodily functions that take a back seat during stress activation.

If this third phase of the stress activation and response cycle fails to take place, we lead our body into a false sense of security, the bar for what our body perceives to be a 'normal' level of activation is raised. So we assume we're relaxed, but actually we're still caught in a chemical soup of activation.

When this constant pinging of the sympathetic nervous system becomes dangerous to our health the Dorsal Vagal nerve is activated - it's basically a safety mechanism to put a cap on an unsustainable level of stress. I mentioned it earlier in this chapter as Dorsal Vagal Shutdown - let's take a look, Dorsal Vagal is just there to tell us that it's a branch of the vagus nerve that runs towards the back of the spinal cord (the Social Engagement system is often termed the Ventral Vagal Social Engagement System, indicating that it's located to the front (ventral) of the spinal cord).

So really our focus is on the word Shutdown. Notice too that it plays a part of the Parasympathetic nervous system, NOT the sympathetic nervous system and that tells us a lot - this is no binary, on/off situation anymore, there is interplay within the branches of the nervous system. When Shutdown comes to town there's a couple of ways it shows up. You might have heard of the freeze response, where you seem to shut down like a rabbit in the headlights. The second way is seen in lethargy, hopelessness, shame, procrastination, and the like. It's that weird state of overly chilled behaviour - you know, those people where you think 'why aren't you reacting? How can you be so calm?', it's almost as though they've dissociated from the situation.

You may also have noticed it in a friend or family member as a rapid outburst of explosive anger, directed in a scattergun effect no matter whether you are part of the problem or not. Self preservation methods such as these are survival states. But they come with a huge down side, leaving the person who has experienced the stress sensitive to pain, and shifting them into experiencing the world from a 'prey state' - they are convinced that people around them are increasingly angry or aggressive, they perceive their reality as being waaay more dangerous than it really is.

Have you ever experienced pain that stopped you from taking part in normal activities? Sometimes it's the result of physical injury, but in some instances there's no rhyme or reason to it. In those cases it's sometimes described as psychosomatic, which is a loaded term in my opinion. It implies that a person might be faking their discomfort, when in reality it's a below conscious mechanism employed by the nervous system to ensure that they stay safe.

In fact, think about how often the term 'psychosomatic' is weaponised, as is 'hysterical' - they're used, primarily describe females, to imply weakness, a lack of rationality, as a prerequisite to relieve the 'sufferer' of their power, and remove them of their responsibility, often placing it into the hands of a more 'capable' (and usually male) being.

Once again, remember that the nervous system is not under rational, logical control. It's a protective mechanism set up to ensure your survival, working at a below conscious, physiological level.

When you are under a great deal of stress, when the sympathetic branch or the dorsal vagal branch of the vagal nerve are activated, you experience greater levels of pain and greater levels of bodily discomfort. You are affected mentally and emotionally so it becomes harder to connect with others, leading to feelings of isolation. It's hard to cultivate heartfelt, meaningful relationships when your nervous system is having a hard time regulating.

It's also nearly impossible to be your authentic magical self when you are occupying a body that is ready for doom, poised for the next inexplicable 'bad thing'. Because even when your active front of mind conscious thoughts are happy and calm, there is a piece deep within you in an alert state.

You may think I'm catastrophising, but ask yourself, where do your lurking fears come from? Those thoughts of not being good enough, or not deserving enough? Where do they originate and where do you hold them? Because these are the modern sabre tooth tigers that will keep you in your cave where you're safe. These are the stories your nervous system is protecting you with when your dreams and desires feel scary. The logical part of your brain knows that there's nothing to be scared of, but the 200 million year old you is devastated by the thought that you may be cast out by your pack and left to the wolves, and sure as shit it's doing its best to keep you safe.

In an age of journaling, Cognitive Behavioural Therapy (CBT), hypnotism, talk therapies and the like, the physical connection is often overlooked. That's not to say that those kinds of therapies aren't helpful, for many people they are, and they can offer greater levels of clarity on what is creating the stress or discomfort being experienced.

But it can never just be about changing your thoughts, beliefs and behaviours, because stress is occurring at a cellular level in your body and your 200+ million year old operating system requires something a bit less cerebral and a bit more primal to help you through. That's why, and we talk more about this in a later chapter, being in nature is such good medicine, especially when we set the intention to be present and aware.

I also think we should chew on why magical, creative nurturing beings such as yourself are constantly being fed a collection of tropes about being 'too sensitive', needing to toughen up or grow up, because there is a cultural sense that there is a 'right way' to do things and we're not managing it.

But before we take a sledgehammer to those societal constructs, I think it's time we spend a moment getting back into our bodies, so we can process and assimilate a new mode of relating to ourselves. This is a process I use when I need to lower my stress response, especially when I notice that I've been hanging out in a heightened state for some time. I found it groundbreaking when I learnt it and I'll always be hugely grateful to the work of Doug Heel[14] for it.

You may be surprised by how simple it is, but don't be fooled, this is powerful stuff. So let's jump up and check in. You'll also find an audio guide for this in the Hot Mess Workbook - don't forget you can access it for free at https://courses.carrieekins.co.uk/courses/hotmessw orkbook

Hokay, so standing up or sitting down with feet on the ground (lying down can lead to snooziness and it's important to stay present.) It's about curiosity, not judgement. There's no right or wrong, we're merely checking in.

---

[14] You can find out more about the Be Activated Technique and Doug Heel's work here https://douglasheel.com/

First of all, I'd like you to think about your breath.
Just watch for a few rounds. Are you having to
remember to breathe? Does the breath feel easy
and flowy or does it stick and you find yourself
having to remind yourself to breathe out?

Now turn your attention to your back, can you feel
the back of your body? Maybe you can feel some
sensation, an ache, a tingle, a tickle, perhaps one
shoulder feels different to the other?

How are your arms hanging if you're standing up?
Are your hands facing palms back or palms to the
side of your legs?

Now turn your attention to your feet. Is there more
weight running down one leg than the other? Can
you feel it in your feet? Is there more weight in your
heels or your toes? Does your entire foot seem to
be making contact with the floor?

Alrighty, you're doing great.

So bring your hands up to your face and I'd like you
to rub both sides of your jaw, and give the side of
your face a rub all the way up to your eyebrows.
Stretch your mouth wide, then give it a waggle from
side to side like a camel.

Next, using just one hand, I'd like you to rub your
sternum, or breast bone - it's the bony bit of you
that runs down the front of your chest, the bit the

ribs connect to. There may be some tender bits, that's okay, just give it a good rub until you notice your breath starting to drop into your chest a little deeper. You may notice yourself sigh, or feel your shoulders drop. It's okay to yawn, or feel weirdly emotional. That's your body regulating, letting go of stress and dropping into a more relaxed state.

Keep on going, rub all the way down until you run out of sternum, now you're going to follow the shape of your bottom rib and keep rubbing so you're on the squishy flesh just under the rib. Do both sides, give yourself permission to get curious about where you're tight and how uncomfortable it is.

Please stay present, try not to let your mind wander to think about what you're going to do next- if you notice yourself wondering, just gently bring yourself back to the breath, or whether you're going to have a cup of tea (although a glass of water after this would be super helpful). Remember right back at the beginning we were talking about the translation of Vagus from Latin? It's 'to wander' and with this simple rubbing technique you have followed the vagus nerve's path - you haven't directly rubbed the nerve, but you have performed an energetic activation - and by doing so, you have helped regulate the vagus response and allowed it to de-escalate and send calming signals back to your brain.

Feeling grounded? Calmer?

Great, now hand me my sledgehammer and let's go smash something! And when I say something, I mean the Patriarchy.

Chapter 6
Boo Hiss Patriarchy!

If you've grown up in a predominantly patriarchal society (hello Western World!) you'll have been subjected to ideas about what makes a 'useful' member of society since the day you were born. It's as invisible as the air you breathe. From the way we talk to toddlers, to the images we see on TV, we're constantly being bombarded with ideas of what men and women should look like, act like, the emotions and indeed the level of emotions that it's appropriate for them to display, and the behaviours they should engage in.

If you're older than 30 then chances are you've been surrounded for the earliest decades of your life by a very subjective media. One that is highly embedded in the male gaze, with a preference for whiteness, maleness and straightness. If you're reading this, chances are that you don't tick all three of those boxes. Which means that the predominant mores of western culture are going to be stacked against you.

Since seemingly forever, the old white guy network has been informing us that there is a necessary division of labour based on gender. You can insert that old trope about women birthing babies and raising children right here. Traditionally, we tick the box of 'good' mothers if we nominate ourselves as the primary caregiver for our womb fruit. Again, traditionally, we are 'bad/neglectful' mothers if we expect other people to care for our offspring for the majority of their waking hours. It is also the expectation that women are 'better' at domestic tasks, so we spend more of our leisure time performing duties around the home than our male counterparts do. This is known as 'Invisible Labour'[15]

This may or may not be the norm in your household. But I'm curious, how many mothers reading this identify with this? And how fucking hard/ unusual is it to have that conversation about leisure time and division of domestic tasks in a hetrosexual home?

Why is it unusual (and blooming hard)? Because we're trained from an early age to abide by arbitrary rules drawn up a frickin' long time ago that serves to place power in the hands of men whilst perpetuating suffrage for women. That doesn't

---

[15] There are many interesting articles and studies on Invisible Labour, here's one to start you off
https://www.mentalhealthatwork.org.uk/blog/the-unpaid-work-imbalance-what-do-you-know-about-invisible-labour/
(accessed on 4/7/23)

make it right, but it is worth reminding ourselves of this truth as women have been blamed, gaslit and denigrated for centuries, so these can be hard conversations to have even with the most equitable of men, added to the fact that it is ingrained in women from childhood so it feels like we're having to break the standard to gain equity.

If you're around the same age as me, mid forties, your mother was a young woman at a time when women were fighting hard and receiving new freedoms. For example, birth control empowered women to take control of their bodies, their pleasure and their ambition.

Contraception gave women the opportunity to decide (admittedly in the early days, only if a man was in agreement and would agree to sign it off at the doctors office) if and when they wanted to have children. This meant that they were able to stay in work longer (there was a strong expectation that once you had children your role would be to stay home and raise them until school age as long as finances allowed), gain promotion, and create the working lives they desired.

It gave women a more equal platform in the work environment. Which is nice, considering how many other challenges there are! Gender equality for many meant the expectation to work as hard, and probably harder, than their male counterparts. As though having a pair of ovaries meant you had to prove your worth. Women were, and still are, struggling for recognition, having to put in more time and effort to receive the same compensation, as their male counterparts. It's as though the same white patriarchs that claimed the power all those centuries ago are still running the show.

And those women were still completing the majority of home tasks. Our mother figures were doing it all! Raising a family, running a home and working their way up the career ladder, until they banged their heads on the glass ceiling. All while wearing full makeup and a kitten heel.

Our mother figures had worked so frickin' hard for this 'equality', and as their children we looked adoringly upwards at them, we couldn't wait to be just like them when we were big! It was the rise of the Superwoman - our mums were (literally) doing it all, running a home and a career with a baby on one the hip, whilst shoving a casserole in the oven with a flick of a foot.

We didn't notice that our mother figures were blooming exhausted. We didn't see that there was little or no time for their own personal pleasure (it is so rarely the case that women of the working class have had much time for their pleasures). But they were expected to be grateful, whilst cooking a proper dinner and hiding their bitterness.

Our generation thought that this was the pathway to greatness. Government policy and the media was happy to corroborate that.

Another cup of burnout, anyone?

Even now, in new industries such as online media, women are expected to put in more time and effort for the same level of return. Particularly in the fashion and music sectors where artists are expected to show up and promote on platforms such as TikTok or Instagram, female artists are finding that their record labels are withholding releasing their new material until particular posting or engagement quotas have been met. It would appear that the same isn't being asked of male artists.[16]

A full time existence, Monday to Friday, 9-5, with the expectation of unquestioned overtime (that goes beyond the bonds of gender), is a productive way of building wealth and fuelling the economy. But it's a shit way to live a life if you're a nurturing, magical human.

---

[16] 'Why Do Female Musicians Have To Fake It On Tik Tok' by Rebecca Lucy Taylor, Self Esteem. Published in The Guardian, 30th May 2022 https://www.theguardian.com/music/2022/may/30/tiktok-female-musicians-self-esteem-rebecca-taylor *(accessed on 4/7/23)*

For many of us it leads to over promising, comparison, fear of failure, overwhelm and ultimately burnout. The old white dude way of doing things does not fulfil us spiritually or at a soul level. It does not bring us contentment. It leaves no space for creativity.

Ironically, this, of course, is often the driving force behind self employed small businesses. Self employed folk start their own businesses because they don't want to work for someone else. The plan is usually to quit the rat race and be your own boss in order to establish a better life/work balance.

It's likely that if you're doing your own thing, it's because you wanted the freedom to do what you wanted to do, when you wanted to do it and how you wanted to do it.

The reality is often different though.

We've been brought up in a society that wants us to believe (amongst other lies): 'Full time good/ part time bad'; 'The customer is king'; 'You have to work hard for your money'; and a million other limiting beliefs that basically scream 'Unless you give every inch of yourself to your business and work your fingers to the bone, you will die penniless and on the streets'.

Anyhoo because of all this shit, these beliefs are floating around in the external environment. You end up working just as many hours, if not more, than you would in a 'proper' job, take fewer days off and find yourself responding to client emails at 3am just trying to 'fit it all in'. Uh oh.

Seriously though, if you find yourself trapped in this quandary, where the 'freedom job' is actually more of a shackle than you thought it would be, I'm here to tell you that it's going to be okay. We're going to work on your boundaries Sweetpea, and everything is going to feel better.

Chapter 7
External Environment vs Internal Landscape

Alrighty.

Here's an idea I'd like you to turn over in your head for a while. To my mind there is a difference between the External Environment and your Internal Landscape and when you learn to discern between the two, you'll be better equipped to deal with any rabbit hole spirals of shame or comparison you may find yourself on the verge of tipping into.

Your Internal Landscape is made up of all the stories you tell yourself that protect you or validate you in some way. Your beliefs, your thoughts, your attitudes, your defences and traumas. It's your magical inner land.

Your External Environment is everything that you have no 'control' over outside of your own being. External Environment refers to the outside world, including but not limited to: the news; opinions of others; the happenings of and on social media; anything with an algorithm; your family; your friends; your work colleagues and all of their points of view and opinions.

Without realising it we soak up that External Environment without appreciating that the Environment is shaped by the human hand and often serves a purpose, although this may be a hidden agenda. Sometimes the purpose is twofold - to (1) provide entertainment whilst (2) maintaining societal tropes.

Think about films or television storylines, they're designed to take you on a journey, the best ones are full of emotion and engage you to care and connect with the characters. But as we all know, the good guys are only loveable if the villains are despicable. Too many adorable characters and it's too saccharine to watch. I mean we love a happy ending but you've got to have a bit of drama to keep you hanging in there, hey?

Some of the most memorable characters from the 80's and 90's were the bitches and mean girls. Your Alexis Carrington Colbys and Abby Ewings, heck even Miss Piggy! They showed us we could be rich and gorgeous, but we couldn't be nice with it and in the end it was always about getting the man! That shit sinks in, informing yet another generation of girls that they had to use their feminine wiles, competitively, in a man's world if they wanted to win the ultimate prize - being a man's wife.

Tv feeds us parables of who we are and what we can expect. It's like a playbook of how to be a good wife/mother/daughter etc and what we can expect our comeuppance to be if we get too big for our boots.

In the UK we have certain expectations, for example, that our news media is fair and objective. But who owns the news media? What are the politics of those people? What is their expectation and desired outcomes? Of course, when the media is portraying a world that aligns with our values that makes for easy living, but what if it doesn't? How do we feel? What happens when we feel cheated or disempowered?

As we saw during the global pandemic, the media - social media included - can create division and opposition. There are many versions of the truth out there - and we have a tendency as humans to pick the version that allows us to feel 'safe', and in 'control', especially when we feel vulnerable.

This is the sneaky issue with algorithms, if the developers' desired outcome is to keep you engaged for the longest amount of time possible, it's going to show you more of the stuff that appeals to you. The human brain likes validation and scintillation, hence algorithms are designed to say "Yes, you're right to think that" and "Ooooh, you'll like this too" - algorithms are programmed to the fact that you might like it because it aligns with your worldview or you might like it because it's far enough opposed to your worldview that you feel outraged and scandalised, and therefore validated. Either way, the External Environment is feeding you what you want, which may well be different to what you need.

From overheard conversations on buses to misogyny in pop music, the reach of the External Environment is far and wide, and all of it is designed to feed you information about how to feel, think and look.

So our beliefs are shaped by the External Environment, and yes the two spheres are very much interlinked, but you have control over your Internal Landscape. This is a space that you can watch, observe, monitor and peruse, and in doing so it's worth cultivating a curiosity about the content of your thoughts and patterns of thinking.

When you notice negative thoughts coming up, ideas that make you feel poorly about yourself, judgements against yourself and the like, this is when you get the huge blessing to stop, take a breath, and ask yourself "What evidence do I have for this?" and "How am I sure this is true?".

Your Internal Landscape is shaped not just by the External Environment but also by prior experiences, both positive and negative. If you have had a childhood full of praise and validation you're more likely to be able to show yourself compassion and kindness in the face of challenge or obstacle. If however you've been on the receiving end of trauma or hurt you're subconsciously more likely to feel that in some way you are to blame or be at fault.

One of my favourite quotes is often attributed to Viktor E. Frankl[17] "Between stimulus and response there is a space. In that space is our power to choose our response. In our response lies our growth and our freedom."

The Internal Landscape is where you get to cultivate the space, it's where you get the opportunity to sharpen your practice of choosing your response. It's the home of your intuition and heart felt connection. It's where you get to cultivate your self approval, and love of self. You don't learn to love yourself more because of the beliefs and thoughts you draw in from the External Environment, you learn to love yourself more by trusting and believing in your own self, by feeling good about your own behaviours, beliefs, and morals, by making choices that feel in alignment with how you want to live your life and your values.

---

[17] Curiously, it's from the foreword to a book written about Frankl's work - but the origin is a mystery.
https://www.viktorfrankl.org/quote_stimulus.html#:~:text=Betwe en%20stimulus%20and%20response%20lies,our%20growth% 20and%20our%20happiness. *(accessed on 4/7/23)*

And once you feel in alignment on the inside, within the Internal Landscape, it becomes easier to connect to people that share your alignment out in the real world. But first you've got to work on loving yourself, your good bits, your shady bits, your failures - the whole kit and caboodle. In the words of the great Ru Paul "If you can't love yourself, how in the hell are you gonna love somebody else?".

One of the ways of connecting to your Internal Landscape is by journaling. The act of taking a pen and physically scrawling out the words lights your brain up and can reveal remarkable things.

Throughout this book there are invitations to access the free Hot Mess Workbook full of Printable PDFs. Because it's a PDF the choice is yours. If you prefer to go digital and paperless feel free to just mark them up. However, by printing it out and working through it analog style, with your favourite pen (or even a bit of old ratty chewed pencil) you may find it helps you access another deeper layer of subconscious belief.

Your Internal Landscape has been cultivated throughout your lifetime. When you find yourself butting up against a familiar feeling of "I can't do that" or "I'm not allowed" or any version there of, including that old classic "I'm too stupid", that's a great indicator that it's time to grab a pen and bit of paper and start to get curious about why you think that's the case, where have you heard it, who has been instrumental in setting that belief up for you. It can be a wild ride, suddenly unravelling these bullshit beliefs that you've been absolutely convinced of for years, decades even, but if you're prepared to go there the rewards are huge.

Shall we take a moment and play? Download the printable worksheet from https://courses.carrieekins.co.uk/courses/hotmessworkbook or grab a pad and spend just five minutes writing down the most prominent messages you see in your External Environment and the most prominent thoughts you hold in your Internal Landscape.

Chapter 8
Becoming Aligned

Now we're really getting into the work.

And your magical, nurturing alchemist brain is possibly starting to get a bit worried that it's going to get something 'wrong'. It may even be judging you right now.

Please don't start a judge-fest. All is well.

What I would love you to realise is that it's totally okay not to be a 'career' person, or someone who'll spend their life in an office or even be wedded to one path of employment for life. It's great to be multi-passionate and enjoy new adventures in Income Land.

When I was 15 I read an article about being a 'portfolio worker' i.e. chopping and changing between different roles and types of employment. At the time I could see the scepticism in my mother's face (by the way, this is the woman who banned me from taking a pre university gap year because she was so concerned that I'd get the taste for travel and not come back. She was right in a way - once I graduated University with a 2:1 in Psychology, I turned down the opportunity to join a management fast track with a large British bank and spent almost the entirety of my twenties backpacking around the globe!). Point is, here in the U.K, as far as academic decisions go it seems to be a case of choose well and choose early. If you have any sort of academic potential you're advised not to 'waste it' by fannying around with creative endeavours.

I do think it's changing though. For a start, the cost of University tuition is increasing and the average amount of student loan debt incurred by graduates in 2021 was £45,000[18] - so University is, sadly, not an option for all.

But if you're reading this, and went to university, it is probably a long distant event. Hopefully by now you've paid off your student loans. But maybe you're still stewing in the professional paradox, wishing that you could be doing more of the things that you love and dreading fewer Monday mornings.

Everything in this book is about bringing you more into alignment with the most magical version of you, the one that can enjoy creating ideas and knows which ones needs acting on, the one that can feel

---

[18] According to Statista.com, you can find the full article here
UK student loan debt 2022 | Statista *(accessed on 4/7/23)*

loyal and generous in their relationships without abandoning all sense of self and then feels compelled to fall on their sword of martyrdom. This is about aligning you with the happy, complicated, visionary, playful version that you get glimpses of but up until now has never had the permission to step up and run the show.

But what is alignment and why is it important?

Let's start with a common definition. This one's from Oxford Languages:

> Alignment (noun)
> 1) arrangement in a straight line or in correct relative positions e.g. "the tiles had slipped out of alignment"
> 2) a position of agreement or alliance e.g. "the uncertain nature of political alignments"

Soooo, because I am a massage therapist by trade and therefore a total geek when it comes to bodies, I love the first definition, especially the part about "correct relative positions". Oh yeah, got one leg longer than the other? (most of us have at some point) then you're looking at a pelvis and fascia set up which is all out of whack in terms of its 'relative positions'. In simple terms, to be able to walk, your knee bone is always connected to the leg bone and never the neck bone - right?

In this case though...we're talking about the second definition "A position of agreement or alliance".

Mmmmm...You know those moments when everything in your world is ticking along nicely, you drive through town and all the traffic lights are on green, the friend you were thinking about calls you that same day, your latest blog post reaches your perfect audience and you get great leads and fab feedback? THAT'S Alignment. Like the stars lining up in the sky.

In this book you're going to take an easy trot through simple exercises. Simple but powerful - just like you! Working through them will help you understand what you align with and how to get organised so you can bring it to life.

Alignment to me is about understanding who you are and what you are uniquely awesome at, and on the flip side realising that not only are you absolutely rubbish at certain tasks and jobs but that's TOTALLY okay. Accepting this truth is another glorious step away from being a Hot Mess.

In fact it's more than totally okay, it's a massive relief to know that instead of trying to master all the things, you can just focus on your magic and outsource all the other stuff (to other uniquely awesome beings that shine bright with *those* skills).

My message for you is this: Just be the uniquely awesome Alchemist YOU are, and allow others to support you.

After that we're going to hone in on what is exciting for you to create. I know, I know, you have a BAZILLION ideas (me too hun!) but if you try chasing them all down at once, you're going to chase down nothing. It's a hard truth. But that's just what happens when you have two arms, one brain, one big heart and only 24 hours in a day. That's not to say that you can't achieve them all, au contraire, you can, and you're going to learn how to do that too.

Damn, this is all sounding pretty practical huh? No apologies from me, because here's the thing, there's (almost) always practicality behind any magical experience. And it's possible to make more moments feel magical if you take some strategic steps. Now, don't get to thinking that planning takes the magic out of your existence - instead think of it as an amplification.

Bear with me, especially if you, like many of the wonderful people I work with, are creative, arty, ethereal, but get cold sweats at the thought of being organised! It took me many long years to work it out. I was the Hot Mess that became a lot more chilled through simple strategies (the ones I'm going to show you in this book!).

The simple truth is, when you map out what you'd love to do and create a loose scheme as to how you're going to achieve it, you free up that bit of your brain that slips easily into overwhelm.

Wouldn't that feel like a GOOD THING, because we all know that overwhelm eats dreams for breakfast and wouldn't you rather work to your strengths, rather than painfully trying to strengthen your weaknesses? You deserve to feel fantastically confident and in control, true fact.

Also, in these current 'world gone cuckoo' circumstances, it's really easy to lose heart, feel distracted and end up in a cycle of "Who am I to be a freaking awesome magic maker when there is so much chaos and turmoil out in the world?". Let me tell you this, you have GOT to shine your light.

The world needs you to live full of love and compassion.

We have contracts with our community, to be our best, to be kind, to show acceptance of others - even if we don't always agree. You leaving your best Alchemist self hiding in a cupboard is only going to bring you tears and frustration that will ripple out into the world. Instead, I wholeheartedly suggest that you lead with your heart, have courage and stay curious and open to the wonders of life.

These exercises and techniques are designed to help you understand your unique awesomeness, because when you KNOW yourself, it will ground you. By the power of simple printables, you'll discover not just how to dream and plan, but how to take action and prioritise those dreams. This will give you assured stability when all around things are on the tilt - and that, my love, is worth all the stars in the sky.

Take a moment to journal about your thoughts so far.
What scares you?
What provokes you?
How do you feel about leading with your heart, staying curious and trusting in yourself?

Chapter 9
Watch Out! Someone's Trying To 'Should' On You!

Hands up if you've ever been should-ed all over?!?

You know what I mean..."Ohhh you should totally do this". "No, that's not right for you, you should do this instead", "You should be more like your sister/brother/friend/parent....","Shouldn't you stop messing around with that and get a proper job?"

There's a lot of 'shoulding' going on out there. Most times, people are doing it because they think they have your best interests at heart. Because they care (even if that shows up in a weird way sometimes) and they're scared that you might fail, or that you might get hurt.

This is an interesting phenomena: these 'shoulds' are about the other person's fears and beliefs rather than your capabilities. They 'should' because they're scared of the consequences if they were to do it themselves or because of their previous experience. They want to keep you safe, because what would happen if it went wrong (and sometimes what would happen if it went right).

Humans love to give advice, it gives us a feeling of validation. 'Y'know, listen to me, I know best', when they may actually be unsure as to whether they really do know best, or if they've been half assing their way through life. I mean, who really wants to think they're half assing life? So we give advice, because it feels good. We feel like we're forging meaningful connection, and passing on our hard earned knowledge. Rather than perpetuating myths, trauma and fallacy.

It's more unusual to ask for 'advice' than it is to receive it, am I right? BUT is it really advice if you don't ask for it? I would contend that people will share their opinions for free all day every day, but that doesn't necessarily make it good advice. It's based on their fears, their hopes and their expectations. It will reflect their money stories, or their work ethic, or their thoughts on how to raise children. Whatever it is, it will probably tell you more about them and the way they see the world than it will offer a solution to the situation you're facing.

The crazy part of giving advice (or 'shoulding' all over you) is that most people don't even realise that they're doing it! The even crazier part is that they're doing this because this is how they were raised. Their fears are actually the fears of their parents/guardians, whose fears are actually the fears of their parents/guardians. We pass on beliefs (both positive and negative) from generation to generation all the time without even noticing. It's like intergenerational hot glue, it gets everywhere and binds everything up.

Here's a question to ask yourself - how many times have you listened to well meaning advice and settled for less than you would wish for yourself? We internalise other people's personal fears as our own. Then those beliefs own us. Imagine how it could feel if your successes owned you instead? To your own self be true and all that.

But wait, how the heck is that supposed to happen? How are you supposed to know how to be your uniquely awesome self if you are carrying the burden of other folk's judgement?

Pareto's Principle says that you'll earn 80% of your money from 20% of the work you do. It also rings true that only 20% of the work you do is absolutely truly the work you are created to do, the rest is stuff you could be well placed to delegate or sack off.

Whoaahhhhh...think about all the time you've spent sweating through work that you hate, maybe wasting even more time procrastinating about it, when really, you could be delegating that out (to people who adore it and excel at it) and spend more time focusing on the stuff that truly lights you up and where you shine your brightest.

I get that old adage about strengthening your weaknesses, and it's cool to learn new things, but…if you are suffering through work you hate, maybe there's a good argument to spend that same time making money to pay someone who freaking loves to do it. That makes sense in a strange way, huh?? Even though as the loving, caring, nurturing, people pleasers that we often are, it makes us feel sick to think we can't possibly do everything and be everything that everyone wants us to be!

Sooooo....how are you going to work that out??

To do this we're going to draw on Gay Hendrick's Zone of Genius - you can read more about it in the amazing book 'The Big Leap'. [19] I'm going to talk you through it, the way I interpret it. You can access the workbook to find a handy printable so you can work through it with me.

Set aside some time to get truthful with yourself and let's see what's what. Okay, throughout this exercise I have a couple of questions to hold in mind that may help you feel aligned with your gorgeous, beautiful brilliance.

---

[19] The Big Leap: Conquer Your Hidden Fear and Take Life To The Next Level by Gay Hendrick, 2009

The first is this: 'How do you want to feel about your life, work and creations?'

Say what, Carrie?

This is a different way of looking at the world, usually it's "What do you think about..." or "Do you like your job?". Here we ask, how do you want to feel? This provokes a much deeper part of your brain. Known as the limbic system, or reptilian brain, it's one of the oldest parts of the brain. It's instinctual and creates responses based on emotion or behaviour, rather than logic or rationality.

Think about your first response to a stressful situation (the fight or flight response), that's the limbic system in action. Why do you think baby animal videos are so endearing? Thanks to the limbic system we're wired to care.

And the second thing I ask you to hold in mind is: 'What would you like to accomplish?'

Allowing yourself to sink into a place of inquiry around how you want to feel, and what you would like to bring forth and the ripple it has in the broader world, is a beautiful way to hack into the deeper 'Why' of your work.

In Simon Sinek's mind expanding Tedtalk "How great leaders inspire action", [20] he takes us through the importance of getting up close and personal with the reasons we do what we do. According to Sinek, if you look at game changing leaders such as Martin Luther King, or Steve Jobs for example, one of the reasons why they're so persuasive is because they understand their 'Why' - their reasoning for why they do what they do or why they're the best at what they do. By being in touch with their 'Why' such leaders are able to harness an emotional power which we, the viewer or buyer, feels compelled and moved by thus we want to 'buy' whatever it is that they're selling.

It's never about what you do or how you do it, it's always about 'why' you do it.

This is powerful knowledge. Why? Well, when you understand what makes you tick, and what makes people resonate with it, you can speak to that and in doing so create wonderful change and transformation. I talk through this more with my coaching clients, because when you come from a place of feeling, of truthful emotion, it tickles that old, old, part of the brain and it can be incredibly heart opening for all concerned.

Alrighty, got them?
1) How would you like to feel?
2) What would you like to accomplish?

---

[20] Watch it here
https://www.ted.com/talks/simon_sinek_how_great_leaders_inspire_action/comments *(accessed on 4/7/23)*

You can add an additional question further down the tracks, which is: How would I like to feel when I have accomplished this? (this is kind of a head twist, think about how good it will feel to get it completed)

Let's get to the worksheet, it's in the free Hot Mess Workbook[21] This is how it works:

You have four boxes. I warn ya now, it looks simple, and it IS simple, but that's not to say that filling these boxes in isn't going to mess with your head a little! There doesn't need to be a straight line answer to this exercise, and you can refine, hone, scratch it and start again as often as you like.

Box 4 is probably the easiest to do (annoyingly, we're very good at regaling our faults), so let's start there. The question is, what are you so absolutely rubbish at, that you dislike with such vengeance, that you can't wait to never, ever do again? You know, don't hold back. Not a numbers person? Feel the grip of fear at Tax Return time? Hate creating pretty documents and presentations? Absolutely despise cleaning out the gutters/loading the dishwasher/entertaining the kids?

---

[21] Have you accessed it yet? Here it is: https://courses.carrieekins.co.uk/courses/hotmessworkbook

I know a woman, whose business became hugely successful when she realised that whilst having kids was wonderful, it didn't fulfil her in the way she'd expected. Getting a full time nanny or as she put it, "outsourcing the parenting" created a spaciousness that allowed her to go out and be kickass.

These are the tasks that you want to consider scratching off your list asap, either by delegating them, building systems to get them done quicker, or by making them the 'frog' you have to eat (we'll talk more about frogs later). It's also worth considering if the task you're vacillating on even needs to happen at all, sometimes we just add extra tasks to our list when our brain is in full 'busy busy' mode that comes from a place of overwhelm and maybe a little bit of justifying that "I'm too busy for my life!!". Many years ago, a friend of mine used to point out that perhaps I was 'catastrophising', a horrible term that stung like a slapped cheek, in these situations. I'm sorry to say however, that all too often, she was right!

Oh but the Tax Return bit? Yuh, always make sure your Tax Return is taken care of somehow!

Box 2 is probably the next easiest. Often we are super capable and efficient at a lot of tasks, but they may not make our heart sing. But that's okay. If they are unprovocative but endlessly do-able, put them here. You may recognise that many of these tasks are the ones that fill up your day and bring in the majority of your money … they just don't fill you with desire and delight.

Now we have boxes 1 and 3. Box 3 collects all those tasks where you procrastinate, drag your feet but ultimately get done without too much kicking and screaming (you can look at this list for delegation after box four has been shared out). These tasks are the ones you find mundane but doable. You begrudge them and wouldn't miss them if they weren't there.

Sooo, Box 1. Here we are. What makes you the freaking Alchemist in the room? What could you happily do all day every day whether you are getting paid or not? What are you known for? When people come to you for advice, what kind of questions are they asking you?

If this feels like a tricky box to complete, take a sideways glance at it. For example, if you're on pinterest take a look at your boards and pins. If you read, take a look at your stack of favourites. What could you talk about for hours? What are you obsessed about? Who do you follow on Twitter or Facebook or Instagram (not in the street, that's called stalking).

This is about LOVE in big ol' capital letters.

What do you do that you are passionate about? And here's the thing, there are no wrong answers (possibly some illegal ones). What makes you so uniquely awesome is not socially prescribed and certainly doesn't come wrapped up in the 'shoulds' of other people (or your own childhood conditioning). This is your permission slip of freedom, if you need one.

Just hold in mind those two questions:
1) How would you like to feel?
2) What would you like to accomplish?

Now go for it you lucious Magic Maker, get feeling and allow it to flow out of you and onto the page.

You can find the worksheet in handy, dandy printable form in the Hot Mess Workbook - it's free, and you can find it at https://courses.carrieekins.co.uk/courses/hotmessw orkbook

Chapter 10
Choices, Choices

Oh yeah. I see you.

You are an ideas machine.

Get you on a roll and the good ideas come pouring out of you (and the bad ones too - that's not to say that there's any such thing as a bad idea...). So much creative whizz, so much go go go! You just don't know where to stop.

It's amazing right?

YES! It sure is!

But, weirdly, we've all met someone who doesn't think it's a good character trait. In fact, I'm betting that at some point in your life you've been told at least one of the following:
- You're scatty
- A day dreamer
- You need to keep your feet on the ground
- Get your head out of the clouds
- You find it hard to focus
- You never follow through

- You have a short attention span
- You need to focus (I'm reiterating for those who drifted off!)
- You should try harder
- You're lazy
- You need to concentrate
- You're all mouth and no trousers
- If I had a penny for every idea you come out with I'd be rich!

Annoying! How dare they?? Who are these people anyway??

Problem is, 'these people' tend to be highly influential on our younger selves: a teacher; a parent; a role model; someone whose opinion you give a shit about. And their flippant comments crush you. They make you question your worth, and your ability. They're toxic and damaging to hear as a child, and goodness knows they trip off the tongue all too easily. Remember us talking about Intergenerational Hot Glue? This is a prime example.

Let me take you back in time to the early 80's. I was a bossy kid with massive tonsils. This meant that in addition to the fact that I really enjoyed telling people what to do (which in my opinion, is very different to being insidiously trained by society to do what you're supposed to! But then I would say that having been a bit directive as a kid) and I liked to tell them LOUDLY (because I could hardly hear myself, such was the snot in my auditory system). One day, I clearly remember being handed a keyring by my dad that we'd won from the Warwick Mop Fair. I was five years old. The keyring was of a big open gob with the words "Why does everybody call me Big Mouth". Youch. Don't sugar the turd dad, give it to me straight.

Interestingly, at my grandparents house (my dad's parents) my sister and I were expected to be quiet, tidy children that moved about as much as a footstool. Grandma and grandpa certainly adhered to the Victorian more of "Children should be seen and not heard" (they weren't old enough to be Victorians but it was how they had been raised, how they raised my dad, and how they expected their grandchildren to be brought up - heck, it had worked well enough til then they must have thought!).

Being the youngest sister of two and a snotty child to boot, with a keen interest in directing the activities of the household, I clearly received the message that I was 'too much'. I'm sure that wasn't the intention of any grown ups in my family, but that was the story I told myself. Stories are far more powerful than straight facts sometimes.

Anyone else recognise this?

I avoid the term 'bossy' at all costs with my daughter. I'm not sure boy children are ever called 'bossy'. In male wombfruit, it's seen as leadership ability, a strong character, evidence that they'll 'go far in life'. Well guess what, it's exactly the same for girls - so long as we don't mire them in our old bullshit.

Hokay, so you have a million gorgeous, glorious ideas. Good For YOU! It's how we're made, it's part of our creative magic. So own that shit, you no longer have to be the quiet good girl at grandma's house, sitting in the corner playing with a small but ugly ornament, doing your best to be convenient.

You get to be LOUD, and MESSY and FUN. You get to do anything you want with all those wild plans and projects that spill from your beautiful mind.

The problem is knowing where to start??

That's the million dollar question. Because when you've always been told you're going to fail based on other people's criteria of 'success', it can be a scary proposition.

When you have sixteen hundred ideas that all feel like the newest greatest thing, how are you supposed to decide which one happens first?

Good question! Hard question? How do you decide?

Here's my advice, from one dream-creating-genie to another. Grab your pen and the 'Choices, Choices' worksheet.[22]

When should you use this sheet? Well, it may be that you have a lot of tasks at home you want to tackle. Or work projects. I used to have a horrible habit of starting a job, getting bored, then starting another task. I'd merrily work away until I hit another bump in the road, then I'd be off on task number three. The upshot of it all? Nothing got finished, I'd get frustrated by all the half assery, berate myself, tear myself down and generally feel shit and impotent. So now I follow this process. It really does help a busy brain.

In the top section, list out all the possibilities. Allow yourself to write, write, write. Get them all down, until your brain is dry.

Next, stand up, walk off, make a cup of tea. Drink it. Stick the kettle back on and have another. Maybe a biscuit too. Bit of cake? Lovely, don't mind if I do. Now, return to the list. (Okay maybe just one more slice of cake, a wishy little one...).

When you read back through your list, some ideas are going to sound less convincing than they did before. Perhaps a lot of them...That's okay. Scratch

---

[22] You know where it is!
https://courses.carrieekins.co.uk/courses.hotmessworkbook

them off if you feel the need for a dramatic gesture and release them back into the wild.

Elizabeth Gilbert writes beautifully in her book Big Magic[23] about ideas being akin to viruses or bacteria, a kind of disembodied life form awaiting a human receptive enough to collaborate with it. The way she sees it, some of your ideas just aren't yours to ideate (if you see what I mean), but they'll make another dreamer very happy.

There's a feeling you're looking for in a good idea. A tingle, an excitement. I feel it like a chill across my body, for a copywriter friend it's a weakening of the knees. When you read through your list, you can feel the good ideas. Take note, be aware, there is magic brewing.

If you don't get a feeling, that's totally and utterly fine. Sometimes it takes practice to listen to your intuition and develop your 'gut feel'. Other times it's about reverse thinking it and asking "Would I be disappointed if I didn't get to do....?" If you're going to feel disappointed, then it's definitely on the contender list.

It's funny how creativity works!

---

[23] Big Magic: How to Live a Creative Life and Let Go of Your Fear by Elizabeth Gilbert, 2015

Perhaps we need to apply other important criteria to our consideration:

- Are you in the business of making money?
- Is enhancing your bank balance a biggie?
- If so, which of your ideas offer a resonance with your clients?
- Which feel as though they could feel fun and easy to create?
- Which stir up feelings of passion, excitement, a raringness to get going?
- Which one scares you a little bit (Oh yeah! That's always a good sign)

Making money is a necessity in the majority of lives (oh, to be free of economic entanglements!) but this is about making money in a way that feels fun, delicious, luscious, fulfilling.

Trust me, it's possible. Making money doesn't have to be a drudge. Some of the nicest money I have ever made has come from a place of fun and freedom. Here's where we get to tie all the pieces together into a terrific little bow, go look at the last worksheet you filled in - the one about your genius - see if Box 1 of that gives you any ideas. It's absolutely not cheating to work to your strengths and your passions.

Now, the hard truth is that on the face of it, some of the most exciting ideas are going to appear to be the most taxing to bring to life. You can run up a list of reasons (excuses?) as long as your arm remarkably quickly.

Such commonly heard reasons (excuses) include:
- They may be expensive to get going,
- It requires IT skills greater than you think you have,
- There's not enough hours in the day
- You're worried about what people may think of you.
- It's not what people know you for.
- You have family commitments and priorities.
- Who would listen to you or be interested.
- You're not good enough/smart enough/capable enough…

That's okay. If you are really hooked on an idea, there will be a way to surmount all obstacles. In the meantime, bump them back down the list and see what else feels good and doable.

Also, have a listen to the language you use to rationalise your decision. Is it coming from a friendly helpful voice, or do you need to unpick where the block is coming from? Often underneath the reasonable sounding excuse is an old standard such as "You're just not good enough" or "What will people say?" - these are the stories you've been telling yourself that come from the external environment but have weedled their way into your internal landscape. You get to rewrite the tune, you get to reframe the story, you get to go out there and BE AWESOME!!!

Ultimately, pick your two favourites. So...now what?

Well, it's back to your overarching criteria, as we discussed above. Is it income? Is it coming from a deeper motivation? Is it to enrich the lives of the clients you serve? Is it to enrich the lives of those closer to home? Does it come from a place of necessity? Or joy? Or both? (Here's a shout out to my brick patio! Oh how you bridged the muddy garden gap and at the same time the act of cleaning each brick and laying it down was strangely pleasing).

At the end of the day, you get to decide. And only you. Wow! That can be frustrating, huh? Remember, you can go back to the list and create the next one as soon as you've done with this one.

But please, get this one done first!

Ha! I know you! I see you!

There you go thinking you can develop two ideas at the same time! "How hard can it be?" "How much time can it take!". That, my friend, is the high road to disillusionment and disappointment.

Uh huh, I've taken that turning often enough.

As boring and pedestrian as it sounds...choose one and get it done. If you really need the pressure, put a deadline on it. In fact, hold on, I'm off to add you a little box to the worksheet, so you can exercise that itch.

(Please if, however, deadlines make you feel queasy, don't feel as though you have to use the box. Although maybe take a moment to see if you can decode why deadlines make you wobble, that would be super helpful for your human existence, because deadlines will always come knocking).

Hokay! How're you doing? You've picked a project!?!

Huzzah!! Well done. I'm so pleased for you.

Okay, maybe you need a little longer? That's fine. But as an addendum...get on with it! It's not a life risking choice (although, if it is, please seek guidance from the appropriate source). Nothing is going to happen if you make the 'wrong' choice. But if you make no choice, NOTHING WILL HAPPEN. Nothing will change. You are responsible for your change. That's a very cool thing. You get to choose. You get to steer your ship.

We all know that completing tasks is hard. So do you want a top tip? Find a friend and tell them your plan. Tell them when you intend to do it by, and ask them to lovingly check in with you along the way.

I'm an Alchemist, you're an Alchemist, we both know that deadlines suck- but if it really matters to you, if you really want to see the task through, get some accountability. I hold my hand up to say that this book would not get written if it wasn't for my mate Kate Arbuckle. Kate is waiting for this book to drop into her hands. If I was left to my own devices it wouldn't get done (trust me, I've been 'writing a book' for six years now) but Kate is expecting it, and she's not going to be mad if it's 'late' and she's not going to judge me if it's a bit wonky. I KNOW that she's going to be bloody delighted for me. And that matters to me.

So yeah, top tip - Find yourself a Kate.

Even if the challenge ahead seems herculean, that's okay, just take a step, even if it's just a little one. But start. Because the world needs your particular unique awesomeness, it really does. It's a divergence of voices that makes the difference, changes behaviours and creates beliefs that enrich the lives of all for the better.

*Whilst we're here, may we talk a little about grabbing a pen?

I always create printables that aren't going to rob your printer blind of ink. I do this because it is important to connect hand to pen and pen to paper. This is something I talk about in my e-course

Letters to Your Badass Future Self[24] and it's worth mentioning here.

Now, research has shown that there is always a connection across both sides (hemispheres) of the brain no matter what the task. BUT handwriting, particularly flowing joined up or cursive script (as opposed to printing letters) uses more parts of the brain than typing. You also retain more information when you write instead of type.

With more connection across the two hemispheres of the brain you get more scintillation, and if we encourage ourselves to think in new ways we create more brain pathways. This in turn produces feel good chemicals, there's a pleasure surge attached to completing new tasks.

Not only this, creativity is mediated by the brain's temporal and frontal lobes. So the front and back of the brain are stimulated by writing, as well as the left and the right. When you use the left and right at the same time you improve language and memory function. Our innovative skills are enhanced, meaning we analyse problems and solve them with 'out of the box' thinking.

Joined up handwriting also encourages visual thinking and deeper thought, involving the body,

---

[24] You can find it here
https://courses.carrieekins.co.uk/courses/letters

mind and spirit. There is a harmonious flow that generates a sense of wellbeing. You develop neuroplasticity - this means it keeps your brain limber and encourages the creation of new Synapses, those clever little junctions between the nerves that need to be cracklin' and poppin' and workin', workin', workin'!

Every person I've ever met who has a dream or a yearning to grow, create, expand into their potential, has felt fear.

One of the biggest crushers of dreams is a sense of not being 'good enough', 'clever enough' or 'capable enough'. Take this as an opportunity to have a little think about the way you speak about yourself, and to yourself. It's frighteningly common to run ourselves down. You may be in a habit so ingrained that you don't even notice it's happening.

This is the point in your life when you can choose to take a stand for yourself and to give yourself credit for your talents.

My love, I am figuratively looking you right in the eye here, when I say you are smart enough, you are good enough, you are strong enough, you are resilient enough, you are persistent enough, you are beautiful enough. You are enough in all the ways. You're here, reading this, because you are a freaking gorgeous shiny Unicorn of a human. In your heart you are fully aware that you are magical.

You've been waiting so long for everyone else to recognise this, now it's time to realise that this is an inside job. Your gifts are special, and they are required on this planet right now.

So let's get that started, I'm here to help you.

Let's go fill in the next worksheet 'Choices, Choices! Which crazy, amazing idea first?'

Chapter 10
There's A Lot Of Bricks In Rome

There's a thing I mutter to myself quite often 'Rome wasn't built in a day, but everyday bricks were laid'. I hate to be the bearer of bad news, but a lot of getting what you want in life is about consistent action.

Gaaaaah! I can't believe I'm even writing about this. It's the bloody antithesis of everything magical isn't it!?! And yet the myth of the 'overnight success' is so prevalent, and fucking toxic.

Even the gorgeous, magical Unicorn that is American pop royalty, Lizzo, is very clear that her 'overnight success' was eight years in the making[25].

I've been in a fair few business development circles over the years. I've seen the yearning in business owners' eyes when they hear other shiny, happy entrepreneurs say " We went from making around £12k in our first year to a six figure turnover in our second year". The comparison monster starts running rife, you judge your actions, you judge your

---

[25] Need inspiration? https://uproxx.com/music/lizzo-overnight-success-road-top/ *(accessed on 4/7/23)*

inactions, you judge the whole kit and kaboodle. Trust me, you can waste a lot of time and a lot of sleep wishing your business was bigger, more productive, more like their business.

But what you don't see is the back story. You hear about the overnight successes and you don't hear about the burnout, the four previous ventures that failed, but ultimately built them a wealth of experience and customers waiting to return.

Yes, overnight successes happen, especially in the tech sector. But please don't think you're failing because others are rising. Certainly you can ask yourself, 'What are they doing that I could emulate?' But also ask, would this feel good for me? Would it honour me and my business? Would it honour me and my family? There's no point copycatting and there's no point dragging your own mental health into the ground.

So I mentioned taking consistent action, it's a hard thing for us magical beings. We struggle with routine and regime. But you can make it a lot less painful, I promise. If you handle everything yourself - no assistance, no team, then try chunking your time. For example, in my business I spend two or three days a week working with clients - let's call this 'working in my business' and then the other days of the week I'd work 'on' my business, during this time I'll do admin, follow up with emails, call clients, set aside some time for study and planning for the future.

And maybe it's just me (just joking, I know it's not) but numbers are a scary thing. In the majority of cases, we can trace this numerophobia (yep, that's an actual thing!) back to our school days, it really does fit in with the 'lack of focus/ fear of criticism' thang. The problem with number work is that it needs to be so exact, and that can be a flim flammy concept at times. So we hide from numbers, we're scared at what our accounts might show us. After all there's no clearer measure of success - how much ready cash do you have? How much debt?

We're qualitative thinkers, the quantitative chills our bones, and yet it's useful to look at numbers so we can see how far we've come. Particularly if we want to set goals and smash them up big time.

For years I thought of goal setting as the evil twin of the business spreadsheet. Together they wreaked havoc in my mind. After all, what was scarier than seeing how much money was flowing in your business versus how much more money was flowing out? Well it turns out that setting a goal and not hitting it was waaay more scary!

When we think about goal setting for our businesses we often reach for the stars. We want to see our businesses grow obviously, but sometimes we overestimate what we can achieve in a short period of time. And that's okay. For many years I used to have a goal of £100,000 a year business income. It was a massive jump from where I was, at around £25,000 a year. I didn't hit the goal. It sucked. I felt on the edge of desperation, and it made me doubt myself. Why didn't I hit my goal? Primarily because I wasn't clear on what I wanted - hence why I'm sharing with you the process I used to get clear about it. It was also because I wasn't taking consistent action, which is definitely linked to not being clear on what I was offering or who I was offering it to.

I hated looking at spreadsheets. I HATED it.

Which made me think.

If I'm such a touchy feely person, why am I signing up for something that leaves me feeling cold? I don't have to do it. No one is forcing me. Convention suggests it's the thing to do. But surely there's a way that feels more playful?

Yep. And it came in the form of cats.

100 of them in fact.

You'll find my handy dandy '100 Cats Are Go!!!' printable in the workbook. It's literally what I do to track my progress. It can be used for anything, so long as you can break it down into 100ths.

The idea isn't a new one, in fact I'd been using colour in trackers for years to manage my daughter's excitement - y'know, how many days 'til holidays, how many sleeps 'til Christmas. She gets so bonkerdoodles about any fun event that she turns into a sleep free beast. It's exhausting, BUT once you put a bit of structure on the timeline it helps her to moderate her expectations.

Say I want to hit a goal of £5000 income in a month. Each cat represents 1% of the total, which in this case is £50. That means that every time I bring £50 into my business I colour in a cat. £350 is 7 cats. £500 is 10 cats. Get the idea?

It's way more fun than a spreadsheet.

Chapter 11
Work Your Magic

Maybe you can relate. A few years ago I made a commitment that I wanted my business to be more productive, to make me the kind of money that meant I could be comfortable without being at work all the time. I was a super successful therapist, working in a way that was creative and full of curiosity. My clients were certainly at the centre of my working world and they were getting the best from me.

I realised for this to be sustainable, there was a necessity to shift how I worked. I was so caught up in my client immersed world that I wasn't paying attention to how I was getting my message out there. At times, behind the scenes was a bit of a disorganised slog. Sometimes, that's the thing about being passionate about what you do, it can take up a lot of energy. As a result trying to get your brain to find space for other important stuff such as marketing and accounts can be overwhelming.

I was bumping from task to task - seeing a client here, trying to finish writing copy there, planning to do a this and a that and the other. All of this whilst also trying to juggle getting diy and jobs done at home. It was starting to bend me a bit out of shape! Ultimately, it was making me less productive and more stressed.

And nobody needs more stress. You don't. I don't.

No one does. Am I right?

Have you ever had that minor tantrum? You know the one, where you wail that you are a creative heart, that your soul can not be tethered by systems and spreadsheets. Such drama! Oooh I've loved a fair bit of that drama! I'm not really a spreadsheet fan, they feel flat, and hard to grasp, like a penny on a very smooth table. But mostly I think I was just scared that I couldn't be organised, and when I failed at it people would roll their eyes in a "what did you expect" kind of way.

After a few of these soul sucking spats, my mentor at the time staged a mini intervention. She could see my potential. She understood what I wanted to achieve. She could see that I was a hot mess, chasing myself around in circles to the point that my head was getting stuck up my bum.

And I think you'll agree, it's hard to get anything done with your head stuck up your bum!

Enough is enough she said. You need to allow yourself to be organised and drop the story that planning is a shackle. Because here's the kicker, she said, you are going to get a hell of a lot more done, when you know what it is that needs doing.

Shit. She was right. The simple act of making a list and ticking the jobs off creates a wonderful feeling of being in control of your world.

Over the years, I've refined my process, and it is a simple one. No expensive software required. No need for in depth project management. It's super freaking simple. Not only that, when I spend 20 minutes on this sheet at the beginning of the week, not only do I know what needs to happen to get a task completed, I can see what needs to take priority.

Priority is an interesting one too. You get to choose. Is your priority to make more money? Is your priority to have more free time? Is your priority to focus on creating something new? You can totally set this up with this sheet - there's even a little bit to circle at the top.

I've made the sheet as unique as us Alchemists. There's a cool little bit on the top line where you can put a word as a reminder of how you would like to feel during the week. It calls you back to your centre. I often put Spacious on my sheet - it reminds me to take breaks, play, say no to the tasks that don't serve me, or to go for a walk. Just seeing one word at the top like Efficient, Satisfied, Confident, Connected and so on, will help you stay energetically connected to the feeling - try it!

Here's how you use the sheet.[26]

Step 1.
Grab a print out of it and four coloured markers or highlighters - these will be super helpful in a bit. First job is to list out in the main box all of the tasks that need to get done. Everything. Tasks for work, home, family, hobbies and passion projects. List them all out. Keep going (and don't be afraid to add extra ones on later).

Hokay, once you've listed out all the tasks, read through your list and ask which ones are truly necessary? Are there any you can scratch off the list (you may be surprised). Next grab your 'free time' coloured highlighter (this is highlighter number 1) and mark out all the tasks that you'd like to get done but don't need doing until you have time off.

These are your lowest priority tasks in terms of productivity.

One of the biggest stumbling blocks of a traditional to-do list is that you either a) tend to work down

---

[26] It's here! It's here! Grab the printable at https://courses.carrieekins.co.uk/courses/hotmesworkbook

them top to bottom or b) pick off all the easy tasks first (ahem). This isn't necessarily going to maximise your productivity. If you've read Eat That Frog!, Brian Tracy's book on dealing with procrastination, you'll know these are your 'Frogs' - tasks that you don't necessarily want to do, but you're spending way too much time thinking of ways you can avoid them. List out your frogs and be prepared to eat them!

Now let's turn our attention to the things that must be done soonest - those with a cold steel imminent deadline. Your highest priority tasks of the week are those with an imminent deadline, your 'frogs', and the tasks that are going to bring money in. Mark all of these with your 'Must do now' highlighter (highlighter number 2)

Time for highlighter number 3! This is the must do soon pen. Mark out all the ones that aren't top priority but need to get done - anything with a deadline lurking on the horizon, projects on the go and stuff that feels important but isn't biting your bum!

Your final highlighter (number 4) is 'It can wait til later' - new project? That goes here (until you get some shit done), less pressing tasks can go here too.

Congratulations on triaging the shit out of your list!

That's the hard bit I promise.

Step 2
You'll see that as you review the list, the tasks naturally fall into categories. You might have home, work, a couple of projects - you'll see. You only have 5 columns - so you may need to prioritise your categories.

By now you'll have a feel for what needs to get done first. AND you'll see that some tasks in this category are of higher priority than others. So transpose them across, listing highest to lowest priority.

If you get stuck, ask yourself what would be 'nice to do' and what do you 'need to do'.

Step 3
Some weeks this is enough for me. I can see what I need to do and what needs to happen next. Other weeks I need more steering. This is where the bottom line comes into play. Each day you are going to pick a 'frog', plus two more important, get 'er done tasks, you then write them down in the daily box. You can also use the daily boxes to plan out your week ahead - play with it and see what works best for you. The way I look at it, if I get these three done each day then anything else is a bonus.

Now I run my work life on a Monday to Friday basis (kind of...I am open to variation) which means my Saturday and Sunday are considered free time. But feel free to doctor this to suit your week. Whichever way you organise your working week, make sure you build in down time and don't feel the desperation to conquer all peaks!

Seriously, my magic making lovely, take the pressure off yourself, you may well be a high achieving alpha tiger who NEEEEEDS to get more than three tasks done, but that can feel really overwhelming (and I hate to say it, can lead to burn out). So pick three and enjoy the glow of achievement if you do more!

Here's another important thing about getting stuff done. Some weeks are 'GO! GO! GO!' and other weeks you don't have the energy for that. RESPECT THIS. Forcing things to happen when you need to sleep, rest or create does not a happy Alchemist make.

Also, whilst we're here a quick note on rest. Rest is an underrated part of getting shit done. Time off nourishes you, gives your brain the opportunity to process and make sense of new information. When you rest, either actively or passively, you create optimal conditions for body repair and growth (on all levels - physical, mental and emotional). We're going to talk more about the power of rest in a bit, when I regale you with the secrets of Tomato Saucery.

Please don't deny yourself the joy of being human. No matter how much work needs to be done, you're not a machine. You need social interaction, humans are pack animals, we're wired up to thrive in tribes. Our brain's requirement for touch makes it a fundamental part of our wellbeing. A 20 second hug sets off a surge of oxytocin - an important hormone for regulating happiness.

In fact, why not schedule in time for connection? A coffee with a friend, a massage, a networking event, whatever you fancy. If you find your work ethic freaking out about the idea about taking 'time off', let me offer you this reframe: You're a social animal. Even the most introverted of us needs to reflect in the mirror of community from time to time.

I received some coaching from a hypnotherapist a while back, and it was by watching the myriad of shock, surprise and confusion on her face (Ha! Trust me, this woman had NO poker face!) that I realised how gunky the old beliefs were that I'd been carrying around like a sack of rotten spuds. What I'm trying to say is that being with other people helps you reset the needle on what crazy looks and feels like sometimes! It can feel like a huge relief to realise that other people feel the same way that you do, and other people recognise the immense strain that you've been soldiering your way through - even when you don't. It's hard to operate in a vacuum, and it can feel incredibly isolating, but it doesn't need to be like that.

Hokay! So the biggest thing to remember is that even though you listed a hundred and one tasks, there is no expectation to get one hundred and one tasks done in a week. At the beginning of the next week, simply transfer across all those tasks you didn't get done and add on new ones (this is why it's okay to add tasks during the week, it serves as an aide memoir - oooh la laaaa!).

You're never going to finish the list and THAT'S OKAY. Each week you'll find that your priority shifts. You'll find this within the space of a couple of days too. Tweaking your plan is what life is about - you'll still be heading in the right direction.

I've said it before, I'll say it again, Rome wasn't built in a day, but everyday bricks were laid.

The upshot of this quick planning activity is having a physical thing to return to when you start to feel overwhelmed. It'll stop you feeling like the sky is falling in, I promise.

But WAIT! Let's return to the eating of the frogs for a moment. Life is about balance, EVERYTHING is about balance. So yeah, getting those big scary tasks done and dusted is tremendous. It can give you a buzz. It can build your confidence. It can even, sometimes, make you feel as though you are winning at 'adulting'.

However.....

Feeling anxious by how big your list is? Then yes, of course, find easy tasks and get them ticked off (then reach for a manageable Frog to eat). Oh and ticking them off is so rewarding - which is why this is a printable. I said it earlier and I'll say it again and again, there is something about handwriting that allows our brain to make sense of our world better than typing - if you're interested in learning more about this, try my journaling course 'Letters To Your Badass Future Self' and heck, who DOESN'T like ticking a thing off a list??

Speaking of which, you have successfully read this section, but before you move on to printing out and getting cracking with your magic, tick here :

This is so exciting!! Let's continue onwards!

If you get into the habit of setting aside just 10 minutes first thing on your first work day of the week, or even the last ten minutes of the week (sometimes it works best if you get all your thoughts out straight away, then you can sashay off on your rest days knowing you're all set up) either way you choose you have the tool to get your magic cracking for this week and every week to come!

Why not print off a couple of copies of the weekly planner worksheet, that way you'll be able to turn this into a hassle free habit. You can find it at https://courses.carrieekins.co.uk/courses/hotmessworkbook

Chapter 12
The Secret Of Tomato Saucery

Dearly beloved, we are gathered here for a moment of reality. Wanna have a think about your week and take a guess at how many hours you spend sitting at a laptop? You might be sitting at a desk, the kitchen table, on the sofa with it balanced on your knees, any which way. Have a think about how much of your week is spent completing admin, or learning from an online course, researching and the like?

And of those hours, how much of that time is spent sneakily scrolling through websites or on social media, which you loosely justify to yourself as being 'work tasks' or if you're honest pure ol' procrastination.

Incidentally - when you find yourself scrolling for the sheer sake of scrolling (hello Instagram, I'm looking at you TikTok!) this can be a breakthrough question to ask:

"Am I hungry?"

I recently spotted my pattern that I lose concentration for a task and give myself a 'little break' of social scrolling which turns into a pointless, soul degrading 20 minutes. It's only after I start feeling ratty and annoyed with myself because I realise I'm still sitting at my frickin desk and I still haven't moved on with my task, and in reality I'm actually hungry, which is why I couldn't concentrate in the first place!

If you know that you are literally unable to function by 10am if you haven't eaten breakfast, then this is always an excellent question for you to ask of yourself - I am so ruled by my stomach, the world is truly grateful when I've eaten, it's a lot less messy for everyone!

Hokay, are you surprised by how much laptop time you spend?

Does it feel in alignment with the amount of work you're actually getting done?

Many of us were brought up with the idea that you sit down to work and you stay there until you get it done. No matter how long it takes. You're there for the duration.

It starts young doesn't it? Homework, exam revision. Then as you get older job applications and tax returns. You sit yourself down and you get 'er done.

Have you noticed though, even when you start off super productive and you're getting shit done, the longer you sit there, the less 'useful' work comes out? You can be productive for a certain length of time - this is around 45-50 minutes, as long as the average adult concentration span, and then your mind wonders, you start spouting any ol' shit, you mess up, get frustrated.

It's the law of diminishing returns in action.

So how about you try a new way? Because as magic makers we get to respect our uniqueness and we don't need to stick with old paradigms that don't work for us. (Smash the Patriarchy!)

This idea of working a chunk of time and then taking a break is called a Pomodoro. I have no idea where the term comes from, I could probably google it, although it's certain to lose a bit of magic that way! Aaaaand if I do, I may end up in a pointless scrollathon.

For me the word Pomodoro reminds me of Italian Tomato Sauce, in fact I'm reliably told that 'pomodoro' means 'tomato' in Italian (that'll be why then!). Why yes, I am completely driven by food! Hence the 'saucery' - geddit!?

In terms of productivity a Pomodoro is a stint of 45-50 minutes followed by a 10- 15 minute break in which you get up and leave whatever you've been working on alone.

Why the break? Why not just take five minutes? Firstly, it's impossible to make a decent cup of tea from scratch in 5 minutes.

But really, have you ever noticed that when you walk away from a problem or a task and stop thinking about it you come up with the most genius solutions? Ever have moments of break through when you're washing the plates or having a shower? Even if you're taking a stroll through the park your subconscious is mulling it over, and then PING! Magic INCOMING!!

There really is no reason to stay sat down and stuck. You could be enjoying yourself instead.

Here's some ideas of what you can do to create 'saucery':
-   Go for a walk
-   Move your body! Dance, stretch, do a body pump class
-   Roll around on the floor
-   Lie on the grass
-   Take your socks off and stand outside with a cup of tea
-   Write a gratitude list
-   Do the washing up
-   Have a shower
-   Give yourself an orgasm

- Get someone else to give you an orgasm
- Make a necklace
- Play with the cat
- Walk the dog round the block
- Meditate
- Eat cake!

The other upside of Pomodoro-ing your day is that you can set the expectation that you will complete a specific task within a 45 minute chunk and it's MIRACULOUS how often that happens. You really do get shit done faster.

Here's the pro tip though. You need to announce your intention to the Universe, or Divine Spirit or your cat, "Hey, I'm gonna smash through this month's bookkeeping in the next 45 mins. Lets Goooooooo!"

You know what this means, right? When you're done, you're done! Your working day can be shorter, so you can swan off and please yourself however which way you wish. Amazing!

It feels so fucking freeing to know that you don't have to work 9-5, Monday to Friday, PLUS you don't have to sit at your desk all boring day. Who decided that we should adopt that regime for working? Old Dead White Men, that's who. Aaaaand does that fit with the way our lives work now? Nurrr urrr. Because we're working our magic, not living to work.

Chapter 13
Nature Is A Medicine

I sat down to write this chapter. Typed out the possible heading and sat back. Then I rose from my chair and headed downstairs - not to the kitchen to make another cup of tea but to the garden. I peeled off my socks and stood on the damp grass, moving down the lawn to a sunny patch.

I raised my face to the warm beams and had a quick check in. What could I hear? A cement mixer churning a couple of gardens down. What could I feel? The warmth of the sun and the softness of the grass after a night of heavy rain. What could I smell? The unmistakable scent of smokey wood, the butchers on the street front must be making bacon. I plucked a raspberry from the bush and tasted the sweet tang of it. All around me the garden looked lush and green, and so I turned my attention inwards focusing on taking a few deep breaths, visualising sending the outbreath down my legs, out through my feet and into the ground.

How did I feel? Grounded, vibrant, ready to write.

So here I am.

Feeling clear and focused.

When we think of nature we imagine the countryside, the woods, a hedgerow, native flora, birds and animals. Personally, I'm a strong proponent of 'work with what you got' - because it can be surprisingly good, and if it sucks? Well, move on to something better - it's all good.

I live in Sheffield, a city that feels like a string of villages. Where I live, we're on the cusp of the Peak District, a blimmin' majestic stretch of nature if you will. Sheffield is fondly known for having more trees per person than any other European city. I love the woods, we have a blend of ancient and cultivated woodlands, they tell the story of a growing community. In fact I can walk to deep, verdant trees in less than 10 minutes. I absolutely fackin' love this.

In terms of workload and necessary tasks some days are fuller than others though and the invitation to roam gently amongst the beeches and oaks for hours on end must be regretfully declined. That's not to say you can't get a quick fix though.

Nature is medicine for many. Much has been written[27] and said[28] about the effects of nature on

---

[27] I thoroughly recommend reading 'The Wild Remedy: How Nature Mends us - a diary' by Emma Mitchell, 2018
[28] If you have access to BBC sounds have a listen to the first part of the All in the Mind episode 'Urban rewilding for

mental health. It rejuvenates us though movement, a brisk walk pumps blood and lymph around the body. But it also rejuvenates us mentally, spiritually and emotionally if we are open to it. There is wonder to be found in recognising the changing of the seasons. Allowing ourselves to be scintillated if we slow down enough to take in the blossoms, bugs and changing light. Even in a built up urban environment, nature is observable.

I feel that when we lose our connection to the outdoors we lose sight of a part of ourselves. We fall into rushing tendencies, allowing our heads to overrun our hearts and intuition. Once we're in our heads it's easier to fall into habits of increased screen time and doom scrolling, leading to comparison, ludicrous expectations, and denial of our own worth (or is it just me? I don't think so).

Being outdoors puts us back into our bodies. I like to get my socks off and stand on the bare ground - even if it's concrete. It helps me develop my feelsense for what's really going on in my Internal landscape. I like to check in with all of my senses, including two extra scintillations that I consider to be senses because they're so important to our healthy function - the first is movement, the second is the esoteric. If this sounds useful, you can find

---

wellbeing, oxytocin and kindness, false alarm crowd panic' from June 2022 (accessed on 4/7/23)

out more about this in my course 'Discover Your Wellbeing Anchors'[29].

If you are a nurturer there's a fair chance that you require the comfort and hush of nature. If you are a magic maker you see beauty and wonder in the changing year. If you are a hot mess you benefit from a calming tonic of fresh air and lush green. Being outdoors provides us with a medicine of huge value, here's some of the ways how:

If you live in the far north of the Western Hemisphere where our winters are long it's crucial to ensure our VItamin D requirements are met, either by exposing our skin to daylight, or by taking a high quality Vitamin D supplement. Vitamin D is responsible for regulating the amount of calcium and phosphate in the body, both of which are crucial for the maintenance of healthy bones, muscles and teeth.

Daylight and sunshine will help to raise your serotonin levels and regulate your circadian rhythm. When we spend so much of our daily lives in artificial light and artificial air, it sends mixed up signals to our brain and pushes us into constructing our days in ways that enforce our division from nature further. Our sleep patterns are skewed by screens and overstimulation. Our brains can be so

---

[29]https://courses.carrieekins.co.uk/courses/discover-your-wellbeing-anchors

scintillated by the constant flow of information coming to us that we are unable to switch off, relax, and rest.

Here's one of my favourite tools for getting out of my thoughts and back into my body whilst simultaneously connecting to nature. Try this next time your thoughts start to spiral into negative places.

The first thing to do is get your boots on and get outside. Your body responds so well to fresh air and movement, aaaaand you always get bonus points if you choose to abandon your desk in search of sunshine on your face. No matter how long you have, ten minutes, half an hour, half a day, take the opportunity to stride out and play 'Blackbird, Pigeon, Magpie, Squirrel! (or if you're in a built up urban situation 'Red Car, Green Car, Chip Shop, BUS!').

The objective of the game is super simple: place your attention outside of yourself. Listen to the sounds around you, feel the path beneath your feet and the air on your face, allow your eyes to seek out tiny details. Here's the city edition:
"Oh look, there's a lizard tank in the tattoo parlour"
"Hey, that flower is blooming even through the crack in the tarmac"
"Whoah, look at the size of that dog/house plant/birdpoop/etc"

Details people, look for the details.

As the name implies, you're looking for the ordinary, and marvelling in it.

Imagine it's the first time you've ever seen a pair of trainers dangling from an overhead wire, or that you've never seen a squirrel before. Take delight in the everyday normal stuff that surrounds you and take it all in, because when you're focussing 'out there' you tend to forget the internal doomscroll of your thoughts.

And if you do find yourself retreating inward again, amp up the wonder and say hello to every friendly street cat and park dog you see (I'm pretty sure I'm not the only person who greets passing dogs as old acquaintances?).

If you'd like to add an extra dimension to the game, utilise the pauses. So where the path splits or there's a road junction, stop for a moment, check in with your posture. How does it feel to be in your body at this moment? If you soften your knees, is it better or worse? If you tuck your bum in, is it better or worse? If you lengthen your spine as though it's being tugged by a string from the heavens, is it better or worse? NEWS FLASH! You can also do this anytime. Like NOW. Go on! Stand up and have a quick body check in. It'll take 10 seconds max.

It felt good, right?

Looking at far off horizons is soothing to the eyes and the nervous system. You don't have to be looking at any great beauty, it's just about giving yourself permission to see beyond your proximity, so let your eyes drift to the horizon and give them a break from close concentration.

Whilst we can't control our external environment, we CAN change how we RESPOND to it. Curate your tools, learn what soothes you, discover simple ways to calm your internal system.

And since we've segued back to the subject of External Environment/Internal Landscape, let's dive a little deeper into your personal cycles and rhythms. The seasons of your life and the ebb and flow of your hormones can make a big difference to how you feel and perceive the world.

Hun, sometimes, in your hormonal cycle, you're going to feel like a Hot Mess, and how you stop it or try to control it will have knock on effects. Our bodies can feel like riotous, chaotic affairs, that wreak havoc over how able we feel to interact with the world.

Society, as created by Old White Men, doesn't like the thought of blood and emotions, it makes it squeamish. Those old rule-setting bastards just didn't know how to connect with it on an empathetic level, so they decided "Sod that! Let's carry on as 'normal'!". So, historically, we ended up in this slightly sinister hole of two genders and no recognition of hormones - apart from Testosterone, which in the view of Old White Men of the West makes you all 'Grrr' and 'Useful' for flexing your literal and metaphorical muscles.

"Who needs Compassion!" the Old White Men of the West shouted through their governance and social positions. "Down with Considerate Behaviour! Let's go force some weaker, poorer plebs and push them around so they make us loads of MONEY!!!"

What a bunch of penises.

In building a world based on Power and Greed they squeezed the compassionate, heart-led, magic making, nurturing instincts out of many. It fed the wolves of Industry and oftentimes it felt like they were using the dead limp bodies of the feminine to do that.

But nature always wins. As Lao Tzu, the smart old dude of the East, said "Nature does not hurry, yet everything is accomplished." If we wish to see a better planet, it's time for Magic Makers like you and I to play our part. Not all Revolution is noisy and war-like, you see.

It's time for us to reclaim our Internal Landscape of peaks and troughs, ebbs and flows. It's time for us to honour that how we feel in our body will relate to how vulnerable we feel in our beliefs and ability to take action. If you are a person born with ovaries, you may have noticed that how your bravery, courage, sensuality, analytic mindedness or any of the other emotional sensations that feed action, changes depending on whether it's your window of ovulation, or menstruation or anywhere in between. If you were born deeply embedded in your feminine then at a deep level you understand the strength of vulnerability and kindness (even if that feels hard to access at times).

Whilst the makers of feminine sanitary products would like to have us believe that our monthly reproductive cycle is a homogenised experience - we know it's not. Just like pregnancy or the fourth trimester is not a homogenised experience either. It's convenient to have us believe that we should feel or act in a certain way. It's convenient to have us feel that if we're accessing different emotions or responses that we're 'doing it wrong'. I'd love for you to build up a compassionate consideration for your body's energetic cycle, even if the relationship you've shared with your body has at times been rough. Be kind to yourself when you require periods of introspection and listen to when your body is telling you it has 'go' energy on tap, it's not required to push and force your way through life.

It's time to listen to Nature, our External Environment and our Internal Landscape. There's a reason why you feel like a Hot Mess, it's because you're acting against what feels good, or 'right' for YOU. No longer should we accept the standardised tropes of our society. Learn to come back into your body through moving your body, connecting to nature, trusting your intuition, and by questioning the origin of the stories you tell yourself.

Chapter 14
Bringing It All Together

So here we are, my lovely magic making friend.
How are you feeling?

Less of a Hot Mess?
More purposeful?
More organised?
More lit up from within?
Slinky perhaps?

Still trying to work it out a little?

I know, it's never as cut and dried as it may appear.
THAT is the WONDER of being human. We are
such curious creatures (yes, I mean that in all the
ways) but that moment of a question being
answered and yet opening the invitation to more
questions and excitement is SO MUCH FUN!

Being in alignment with the biggest, most exciting
version of you (available in your mind at this very
moment - trust me it changes!) is a thrill.
Sometimes you feel as though you can exist there
forever and sometimes it feels like a wisp of a
feeling that gets snatched away from you in a
second.

What I hope you have gained from our short time together is an insight, maybe even a road map. You can see what you wish to create and how you can get it done.

Like I said, there may be, however, bumps in the road ahead. That's okay. In fact that's great. Every bump is an opportunity for enquiry, to learn more about yourself, to let go of old beliefs, gunk and sometimes even trauma. Every bump, if you are prepared to do the sticky work, is an invitation to grow. If you hold on to the tools you've gathered here:
- Nervous system regulation through breathing and activation of your diaphragm
- Creating structure through weekly planning that will create a container for you to return too when you find yourself distracted by other shiny objects
- Recognising your wellbeing requirements, which are as unique and individual as you are
- Treating yourself compassionately when you fall into old habits as prescribed by the External Environment and allowing yourself to tap back into your Internal Landscape then you'll be fine, more than fine, in fact you'll be awesome.

I've been a seeker, a learner, a teacher, a call it what you will...someone who is fascinated by people since I was a child. Our capacity to heal and grow makes me swoon. It's a magical thing to be an Alchemist, putting the magic back into the world, connecting with our Inner Landscape and Nature and all that good stuff.

We are such resilient beings. We are magnificent. And yes, there will still be days when we get distracted and accidentally burn the toast…again…!

If you're ready to be more of your uniquely awesome self and feel that I can help you with that, then come check out my words and offerings at https://carrieekins.co.uk

Whatever path you take, it's been my pleasure to guide you through some of the tools I use. From my infinite loop to yours, thank you.

Big love,
Carrie x

Bio
Who The Heck Is Carrie Ekins?

Funnily enough I often get described as childlike due to my ceaseless curiosity and endless wonder in simple things. I have happily spent a considerable portion of my life doing exactly what I want, for no better reason than it makes me very happy.

Well qualified in never having had a 'proper' job, I fully understand how it is to be creative and full of a million bouncing ideas. I chose to be self-employed. In actuality, I chose freedom. I chose seven years of travel and snowboarding. I chose to upcycle my surroundings to fit my vision. I chose to follow my heart and become a massage therapist specialising in myofascial release (even though I have a 2:1 BSc hons in Psychology). For two decades I have had the absolute delight and fascination of working with bodies, with over 15 years of experience as a specialist Myofascial Release practitioner. It was a natural progression, as I'm very much a believer in sharing knowledge, for me to teach courses and mentor gorgeous alchemists like you.

Why? Because I want to live the life I want to live. One that is full and interesting and subject to change. One that has run on sentences and imperfect grammar.

Don't you ever wonder what you could be? Don't you ever dream about what you could do?

I do. (I know you have too, for too long) Everything you need is right there in you. It's that internal game you've got to master. I can help you do that.

You can find out more about me and my work at https://carrieekins.co.uk

Printed in Great Britain
by Amazon

25367242R00079